COLLE
BRITISH
STAMPS

A STANLEY GIBBONS CHECKLIST OF
THE STAMPS OF GREAT BRITAIN

1992 (Forty-fourth) Edition

STANLEY GIBBONS PUBLICATIONS LTD

By Appointment to H. M. the Queen
Stanley Gibbons Ltd, London Philatelists.

London and Ringwood

COLLECT BRITISH STAMPS

The 1992 Edition

From the famous Penny Black of 1840 to the absorbing issues of today, the stamps of Great Britain are highly popular with collectors. *Collect British Stamps* has been our message since very early days – but particularly since the First Edition of this checklist in September 1967. This 44th edition includes all the recent issues. Prices have been carefully revised to reflect today's market. Total sales of *Collect British Stamps* are now nearly 3½ million copies.

Collect British Stamps appears in the autumn of each year. A more detailed Great Britain catalogue, the *Concise*, is published each spring. The *Great Britain Concise* incorporates many additional listings covering watermark varieties, phosphor omitted errors, missing colour errors, stamp booklets and special commemorative First Day Cover postmarks. It is ideally suited for the collector who wishes to discover more about GB stamps.

Listings in this edition of *Collect British Stamps* include all 1992 issues which have appeared up to the publication date.

Scope. *Collect British Stamps* comprises:
- All stamps with different watermark (*wmk*) or perforation (*perf*).
- Visible plate numbers on the Victorian issues.
- Graphite-lined and phosphor issues, including variations in the number of phosphor bands.
- First Day Covers for all Special Issues.
- Special Sections for Definitive and Regional First Day Covers of the present reign.
- Presentation, Gift and Souvenir Packs.
- Post Office Yearbooks.
- Regional issues and War Occupation stamps of Guernsey and Jersey.
- Postage Due and Official Stamps.
- Post Office Picture Cards (PHQ cards).
- Commemorative gutter pairs and "Traffic Light" gutter pairs listed as mint sets.
- Royal Mail Postage Labels priced as sets and on P.O. First Day Cover.

Stamps of the independent postal administrations of Guernsey, Isle of Man and Jersey a[re] contained in *Collect Channel Islands and Isle [of] Man Stamps*.

Layout. Stamps are set out chronologically b[y] date of issue. In the catalogue lists the fir[st] numeral is the Stanley Gibbons catalog[ue] number; the black (boldface) numeral alongsi[de] is the type number referring to the respecti[ve] illustration. A blank in this column implies th[at] the number immediately above is repeated. T[he] denomination and colour of the stamp are the[n] shown. Before February 1971 British curren[cy] was:

£1 = 20s   One pound = twenty shillings a[nd]
1s = 12d   One shilling = twelve pence.

Upon decimalisation this became:

£1 = 100p   One pound = one hundred (new) pence.

The catalogue list then shows two pri[ce] columns. The left-hand is for unused stamps a[nd] the right-hand for used. Corresponding sm[all] boxes are provided in which collectors may wi[sh] to check off the items in their collection.

Our method of indicating prices is: Numerals for pence, e.g. 10 denotes 10p (1[0] pence). Numerals for pounds and pence, e.[g.] 4·25 denotes £4·25 (4 pounds and 25 pence[).] For £100 and above, prices are in whole poun[ds] and so include the £ sign and omit the zeros f[or] pence.

Colour illustrations. The colour illustration[s] of stamps are intended as a guide only; they m[ay] differ in shade from the originals.

Size of illustrations. To comply with Po[st] Office regulations stamp illustrations are thre[e] quarters linear size. Separate illustrations of su[r]charges, overprints and watermarks are actu[al] size.

Prices. Prices quoted in this catalogue are o[ur] selling prices at the time the book went to pres[s.] They are for stamps in fine condition; in issu[es] where condition varies we may ask more for t[he] uperb and less for the sub-standard. The nused prices for stamps of Queen Victoria to ing Edward VIII are for lightly hinged examples. nused prices for King George VI and Queen lizabeth II are for unmounted mint (though hen not available unmounted, mounted stamps re often supplied at a lower price). Prices for sed stamps refer to postally used copies. All rices are subject to change without prior notice nd we give no guarantee to supply all stamps riced, since it is not possible to keep every atalogued item in stock. Individual low value tamps sold at 399, Strand are liable to an dditional handling charge.

In the price columns:
= Does not exist.
—) or blank = Exists, or may exist, but price cannot be quoted.
= Not normally issued (the so-called 'Abnormals' of 1862–80).

erforations. The 'perforation' is the number of oles in a length of 2 cm, as measured by the ibbons *Instanta* gauge. The stamp is viewed gainst a dark background with the transparent auge put on top of it. Perforations are quoted to he nearest half. Stamps without perforation are ermed 'imperforate'.

Se-tenant combinations. *Se-tenant* means 'joined together'. Some sets include stamps of different design arranged *se-tenant* as blocks or strips and these are often collected unsevered as issued. Where such combinations exist the stamps are priced both mint and used, as singles or complete combinations. The set price for mint refers to the unsevered combination plus singles of any other values in the set. The used set price is for single stamps of all values.

First day covers. Prices for first day covers are for complete sets used on plain covers (1924, 1925, 1929) or on special covers (1935 onwards), the stamps of which are cancelled with ordinary operational postmarks (1924–1962) or by the *standard* "First Day of Issue" postmarks (1963 onwards). Where the stamps in a set were issued on different days, prices are for a cover from each day.

PHQ cards. Since 1973 the Post Office has produced a series of picture cards, which can be sent through the post as postcards. Each card shows an enlarged colour reproduction of a current British stamp, either of one or more values from a set or of all values. Cards are priced here in fine mint condition for sets complete as issued. The Post Office gives each card a 'PHQ' serial number, hence the term. The cards are usually on sale shortly before the date of issue of the stamps, but there is no officially designated 'first day'.

Used prices are for cards franked with the stamp depicted, on the obverse or reverse; the stamp being cancelled with an official postmark for first day of issue.

Se-tenant block

Gutter pairs. All modern Great Britain commemoratives are produced in sheets containing two panes of stamps separated by a blank horizontal or vertical margin known as a gutter. This feature first made its appearance on some supplies of the 1972 Royal Silver Wedding 3p, and marked the introduction of Harrison & Sons' new "Jumelle" stamp-printing press. There are advantages for both the printer and the Post

Office in such a layout which has now been used for all commemorative issues since 1974.

The term "gutter pair" is used for a pair of stamps separated by part of the blank gutter margin.

Gutter pair

Most printers include some form of colour check device on the sheet margins, in addition to the cylinder or plate numbers. Harrison & Sons use round "dabs", or spots of colour, resembling traffic lights. For the period from the 1972 Royal Silver Wedding until the end of 1979 these colour dabs appeared in the gutter margin. Gutter pairs showing these "traffic lights" are worth considerably more than the normal version.

Traffic light gutter pair

Catalogue numbers used. The checklist use the same catalogue numbers as the Stanle Gibbons *British Commonwealth* Catalogu (Part 1), 1992/93 edition.

Latest issue date for stamps recorded in thi edition is 10 November 1992.

STANLEY GIBBONS LTD

Head Office: 399 Strand, London WC2R 0LX
Auction Room and Specialist Stamp De partments—Open Monday-Friday 9.30 a.m to 5 p.m.
Shop—Open Monday 9.30 a.m. to 5.30 p.m Tuesday-Friday 8.30 a.m. to 5 p.m. an Saturday 10.00 a.m. to 4 p.m.

Telephone 071-836 8444 for all department:

Stanley Gibbons Publications Ltd:
Editorial, Sales Offices and
Distribution Centre,
5, Parkside, Christchurch Road,
Ringwood, Hants BH24 3SH.
Telephone 0425 472363

ISBN: 0-85259-338-4
© Stanley Gibbons Publications Ltd 1992

BY APPOINTMENT TO
HER MAJESTY THE QUEEN.
STANLEY GIBBONS LTD
PHILATELISTS

BUYING STAMPS BY MAIL ORDER? MAKE SURE YOU USE THE
STANLEY GIBBONS
MAIL ORDER SERVICE

How we can help you improve your collection

★ SERVICE We can offer you a friendly, highly efficient service supported by over 135 years of philatelic experience.

★ QUALITY The range and depth of our stock is world famous. Most items can be supplied immediately – always of the highest quality and backed by the Gibbons guarantee of authenticity.

★ BUDGET PLANS AND INTEREST FREE payment schemes available to spread the cost.

★ BACK UP STOCK of Errors, Varieties, Missing Colours, Multiples and any number of unusual items.

★ PERSONAL SERVICE from our GB Mail Order Specialist, Ian Boulton.

For further details of how we can help you just contact Ian Boulton at the address below. If you would also like to order some items from our stock simply use the order form overleaf or see the priced lists on the pages at the back of this catalogue.

Ian Boulton, Great Britain (Mail Order) Service
399 Strand, London WC2R 0LX
Tel: 071–836 8444   Fax: 071–836 7342

STANLEY GIBBONS LTD
GREAT BRITAIN
MAIL ORDER SERVICE
ORDER FORM

To order simply fill out the form below (continuing on a separate sheet if necessary). Cut along the dotted line and send it with payment details to Ian Boulton at the address below. **Please use the easy tick box form for Queen Elizabeth II commemoratives on the pages at the end of the book and return with your details.**

Please note that all items will be supplied (if currently available) at the prices quoted in this catalogue, although these may be subject to change without prior notice.

We regret that commemorative stamps can only be supplied in complete sets and that orders totalling less than £10 (excluding postage) are respectfully declined.

To: Stanley Gibbons Ltd Great Britain Mail Order Service, 399 Strand, London WC2R 0LX

Please send me

SG No.	Condition (u/m, f/u, etc)	£	p	SG No.	Condition (u/m, f/u, etc)	£	p	SG No.	Condition (u/m, f/u, etc)	£	p

☐ I enclose cheque/PO made payable to Stanley Gibbons Ltd. for £..............

☐ I have paid £................. into Stanley Gibbons Giro Account No. 586 6006

☐ I authorise you to charge my credit card for £................

Type of card .... (all major cards accepted)

Total		
Postage & Handling	1	50
Total Order Value		

Expiry date

Card No. | | | | | | | | | | | | | | | |

Signature..................................

Name .... Address ....

.... Postcode ....

Please allow 14 days for delivery (overseas customers 21 days)

Please tick if you wish to receive:– Machin List ☐ G.B. Specialised ☐

QUEEN VICTORIA

1837 (20 June)–1901 (22 Jan.)

IDENTIFICATION. In this checklist Victorian stamps are classified firstly according to which printing method was used · line-engraving, embossing or surface-printing.

Corner letters. Numerous stamps also have letters in all four, or just the lower, corners. These were an anti-forgery device and the letters differ from stamp to stamp. If present in all four corners the upper pair are the reverse of the lower. Note the importance of these corner letters in the way the checklist is arranged.

Watermarks. Further classification depends on watermarks: these are illustrated in normal position, with stamps priced accordingly.

Line-engraved Issues

1a

2

2a White lines added above and below head

3 Small Crown watermark

4 Large Crown watermark

Letters in lower corners

1840 *Wmk Small Crown Type 3   Imperforate*

Cat. No.	Type			Unused	Used		
2	1	1d	black	£3000	£150	□	□
5	2	2d	blue	£5500	£300	□	□

1841

8	1a	1d	red-brown ..	£130	3·50	□	□
14	2a	2d	blue	£1000	35·00	□	□

1854–57 *(i) Wmk Small Crown Type 3   Perf 16*

17	1a	1d	red-brown ..	£125	3·50	□	□
19	2a	2d	blue	£1300	35·00	□	□

(ii) Wmk Small Crown Type 3   Perf 14

24	1a	1d	red-brown ..	£225	16·00	□	□
23	2a	2d	blue	£1800	£120	□	□

(iii) Wmk Large Crown Type 4   Perf 16

26	1a	1d	red	£450	35·00	□	□
27	2a	2d	blue	£2000	£130	□	□

(iv) Wmk Large Crown Type 4   Perf 14

40	1a	1d	red	25·00	1·00	□	□
34	2a	2d	blue	£1000	25·00	□	□

5

6 Watermark extending over three stamps

7

8

9

Letters in all four corners

Plate numbers. Stamps included a 'plate number' in their design and this affects valuation. The cheapest plates are priced here; see complete list of plate numbers overleaf.

1858–70 *(i) Wmk Type 6   Perf 14*

48	5	½d	red	45·00	6·00	□	□

(ii) Wmk Large Crown Type 4   Perf 14

43	7	1d	red	4·50	50	□	□
51	8	1½d	red	£150	18·00	□	□
45	9	2d	blue	£160	4·00	□	□

PLATE NUMBERS
on stamps of 1858–70 having letters in all four corners

Positions of Plate Numbers

Shows
Plate 9 (½d)

Shows
Plate 170 (1d. 2d)

Shows
Plate 3 (1½d)

HALFPENNY VALUE (S.G. 48)

Plate	Un.	Used			Plate	Un.	Used	
1	95·00	40·00	□	□	11	45·00	6·00	□
3	60·00	14·00	□	□	12	45·00	6·00	□
4	75·00	8·00	□	□	13	45·00	6·00	□
5	55·00	6·00	□	□	14	45·00	6·00	□
6	45·00	6·00	□	□	15	60·00	9·00	□
8	85·00	40·00	□	□	19	90·00	18·00	□
9	£2250	£300	□	□	20	95·00	30·00	□
10	75·00	6·00	□	□				

Plates 2, 7, 16, 17 and 18 were not completed, while Plates 21 and 2
though made, were not used. Plate 9 was a reserve plate, not greatly use

PENNY VALUE (S.G. 43)

Plate	Un.	Used			Plate	Un.	Used			Plate	Un.	Used			Plate	Un.	Used	
71	12·00	2·00	□	□	112	30·00	1·00	□	□	154	7·50	50	□	□	190	7·00	3·50	□
72	18·00	2·50	□	□	113	8·00	7·50	□	□	155	8·00	75	□	□	191	4·50	4·00	□
73	12·00	2·00	□	□	114	£175	8·00	□	□	156	7·50	50	□	□	192	13·00	50	□
74	10·00	50	□	□	115	50·00	1·00	□	□	157	7·50	50	□	□	193	4·50	50	□
76	20·00	50	□	□	116	38·00	6·00	□	□	158	4·50	50	□	□	194	7·50	5·00	□
77	£50000	£30000	□	□	117	8·00	50	□	□	159	4·50	50	□	□	195	7·50	5·00	□
78	50·00	50	□	□	118	12·00	50	□	□	160	4·50	50	□	□	196	5·00	3·00	□
79	15·00	50	□	□	119	5·00	75	□	□	161	15·00	4·00	□	□	197	8·00	6·00	□
80	10·00	75	□	□	120	4·50	50	□	□	162	8·00	4·00	□	□	198	4·50	3·50	□
81	30·00	1·00	□	□	121	20·00	6·00	□	□	163	7·50	1·50	□	□	199	10·00	3·50	□
82	60·00	2·50	□	□	122	4·50	50	□	□	164	7·50	2·00	□	□	200	10·00	50	□
83	70·00	4·00	□	□	123	6·00	75	□	□	165	10·00	50	□	□	201	4·50	3·00	□
84	30·00	1·00	□	□	124	6·00	50	□	□	166	7·50	3·50	□	□	202	7·50	5·00	□
85	12·00	1·00	□	□	125	8·00	1·00	□	□	167	5·00	50	□	□	203	4·50	10·00	□
86	15·00	2·50	□	□	127	17·00	1·00	□	□	168	6·00	5·50	□	□	204	6·00	75	□
87	4·50	50	□	□	129	6·00	50	□	□	169	15·00	4·00	□	□	205	6·00	2·00	□
88	80·00	5·50	□	□	130	9·00	1·00	□	□	170	6·00	50	□	□	206	6·00	6·00	□
89	20·00	50	□	□	131	38·00	11·00	□	□	171	4·50	50	□	□	207	6·00	6·00	□
90	14·00	50	□	□	132	50·00	16·00	□	□	172	4·50	90	□	□	208	6·00	10·00	□
91	20·00	3·50	□	□	133	45·00	6·00	□	□	173	25·00	6·00	□	□	209	7·50	6·00	□
92	7·00	50	□	□	134	4·50	50	□	□	174	4·50	40	□	□	210	10·00	8·00	□
93	20·00	50	□	□	135	50·00	20·00	□	□	175	18·00	1·75	□	□	211	22·00	15·00	□
94	20·00	3·00	□	□	136	50·00	15·00	□	□	176	13·00	90	□	□	212	7·50	7·50	□
95	12·00	50	□	□	137	8·00	90	□	□	177	5·00	50	□	□	213	7·50	7·50	□
96	14·00	50	□	□	138	6·00	50	□	□	178	7·50	2·00	□	□	214	13·00	13·00	□
97	8·00	1·75	□	□	139	16·00	11·00	□	□	179	8·00	1·00	□	□	215	13·00	13·00	□
98	8·00	3·50	□	□	140	6·00	50	□	□	180	8·00	3·00	□	□	216	13·00	13·00	□
99	12·00	3·00	□	□	141	75·00	6·00	□	□	181	7·50	50	□	□	217	10·00	4·00	□
100	18·00	1·25	□	□	142	25·00	18·00	□	□	182	50·00	3·00	□	□	218	6·00	5·00	□
101	25·00	6·00	□	□	143	15·00	10·00	□	□	183	13·00	1·50	□	□	219	30·00	50·00	□
102	10·00	55	□	□	144	50·00	15·00	□	□	184	4·50	75	□	□	220	4·50	3·50	□
103	10·00	1·50	□	□	145	4·50	1·00	□	□	185	7·50	1·50	□	□	221	15·00	10·00	□
104	14·00	3·00	□	□	146	5·00	3·50	□	□	186	15·00	1·00	□	□	222	25·00	25·00	□
105	35·00	4·00	□	□	147	9·00	2·00	□	□	187	6·00	50	□	□	223	30·00	40·00	□
106	15·00	55	□	□	148	10·00	1·50	□	□	188	10·00	7·00	□	□	224	35·00	35·00	□
107	20·00	3·75	□	□	149	7·50	3·50	□	□	189	18·00	4·00	□	□	225	£1000	£300	□
108	15·00	1·00	□	□	150	4·50	50	□	□									
109	38·00	1·75	□	□	151	13·00	6·00	□	□									
110	10·00	6·00	□	□	152	9·00	3·25	□	□									
111	18·00	1·00	□	□	153	35·00	6·00	□	□									

Plates 69, 70, 75, 77, 126 and 128 were prepared but rejected. No stamp
therefore exist, except for a very few from Plate 77 which someho
reached the public. Plate 177 stamps, by accident or design, a
sometimes passed off as the rare Plate 77.

THREE-HALFPENNY VALUE (S.G. 51)

Plate	Un.	Used			Plate	Un.	Used		
(1)	£350	20·00	□	□	3	£150	18·00	□	□

Plate 1 did *not* have the plate number in the design. Plate 2 was not
completed and no stamps exist.

TWOPENNY VALUE (S.G. 45)

Plate	Un.	Used			Plate	Un.	Used
7	£400	18·00	□	□	13	£180	6·00
8	£450	14·00	□	□	14	£200	8·00
9	£160	12·00	□	□	15	£160	8·00
12	£700	40·00	□	□			

Plates 10 and 11 were prepared but rejected.

Embossed Issues

...ces are for stamps cut square and with average to fine ...bossing. Stamps with exceptionally clear embossing are ...rth more.

11

12

13

...47–54 *Wmk* **13** (6d), *no wmk* (others)   *Imperforate*

	10	6d lilac	..	£2500	£400	☐ ☐
	11	10d brown	.. ..	£2250	£575	☐ ☐
	12	1s green	.. ..	£2750	£350	☐ ☐

Surface-printed Issues

...ENTIFICATION. Check first whether the design includes ...rner letters or not, as mentioned for 'Line-engraved ...sues'. The checklist is divided up according to whether any ...tters are small or large, also whether they are white ...ncoloured) or printed in the colour of the stamp. Further ...entification then depends on watermark.

...ERFORATION. Except for Nos. 126/9 all the following ...sues of Queen Victoria are perf 14.

14

Small Garter

16 Medium Garter

17 Large Garter

18

19

20 Emblems

No corner letters

1855–57 (*i*) *Wmk Small Garter Type* **15**

62	14	4d red	£2250	£170	☐ ☐

(*ii*) *Wmk Medium Garter Type* **16**

64	14	4d red	£1800	£150	☐ ☐

(*iii*) *Wmk Large Garter Type* **17**

66a	14	4d red	£600	38·00	☐ ☐

(*iv*) *Wmk Emblems Type* **20**

70	18	6d lilac	£500	40·00	☐ ☐
72	19	1s green	£650	£140	☐ ☐

Plate numbers. Stamps Nos. 90/163 should be checked for the 'plate numbers' indicated, as this affects valuation (the cheapest plates are priced here). The mark '*Pl.*' shows that several numbers exist, priced in a separate list overleaf.

Plate numbers are the small numerals appearing in duplicate in some part of the frame design or adjacent to the lower corner letters (in the 5s value a single numeral above the lower inscription).

21

22

23

24

25

Small white corner letters

1862–64 *Wmk Emblems Type* **20**, *except* 4d (*Large Garter Type* **17**)

77	21	3d red	£700	£100	☐ ☐
80	22	4d red	£500	35·00	☐ ☐
84	23	6d lilac	£650	30·00	☐ ☐
87	24	9d bistre	£1100	£130	☐ ☐
90	25	1s green *Pl.*	£700	65·00	☐ ☐

26 **27** **28** (hyphen in SIX-PENCE)

32 **33** Spray of Rose **34**

29 **30** **31**

Large white corner letters

1865–67 *Wmk Emblems Type* **20**, *except 4d* (*Large Garter Type* **17**)

92	**26**	3d red (Plate 4)	..	£375	40·00	☐ ☐
94	**27**	4d vermilion *Pl.*		£225	15·00	☐ ☐
97	**28**	6d lilac *Pl.*	..	£350	28·00	☐ ☐
98	**29**	9d straw *Pl.*	..	£700	£200	☐ ☐
99	**30**	10d brown (Plate 1)		†	£12000	☐
101	**31**	1s green (Plate 4)		£650	65·00	☐

1867–80 *Wmk Spray of Rose Type* **33**

103	**26**	3d red *Pl.*	£200	12·00 ☐
105	**28**	6d lilac (with hyphen) (Plate 6)	£550	30·00 ☐
109		6d mauve (without hyphen) *Pl.*	£275	25·00 ☐
111	**29**	9d straw (Plate 4)	£600	£100 ☐
112	**30**	10d brown *Pl.*	£1000	£130 ☐
117	**31**	1s green *Pl.*	£350	10·00 ☐
119	**32**	2s blue *Pl.*	£950	60·00 ☐
121		2s brown (Plate 1)	£6000	£1000 ☐

1872–73 *Wmk Spray of Rose Type* **33**

123	**34**	6d brown *Pl.*	£350	18·00 ☐
125		6d grey (Plate 12)	£600	75·00 ☐

PLATE NUMBERS
on stamps
of 1862–83

Cat. No.		Plate No.	Un.	Used	

Small White Corner Letters (1862–64)

90	1s green	2	£700	65·00	☐ ☐
		3	£11000		☐ ☐

Plate 2 is actually numbered as '1' and Plate 3 as '2' on the stamps.

Large White Corner Letters (1865–83)

103	3d red	4	£300	50·00	☐ ☐
		5	£200	14·00	☐ ☐
		6	£225	12·00	☐ ☐
		7	£275	15·00	☐ ☐
		8	£250	14·00	☐ ☐
		9	£250	20·00	☐ ☐
		10	£275	42·00	☐ ☐
94	4d verm	7	£300	19·00	☐ ☐
		8	£250	19·00	☐ ☐
		9	£250	15·00	☐ ☐
		10	£300	30·00	☐ ☐
		11	£250	15·00	☐ ☐
		12	£225	15·00	☐ ☐
		13	£250	17·00	☐ ☐
		14	£300	35·00	☐ ☐
97	6d lilac	5	£350	28·00	☐ ☐
		6	£1000	55·00	☐ ☐
109	6d mauve	8	£275	25·00	☐ ☐
		9	£275	25·00	☐ ☐
		10	*	£12000	☐ ☐
123	6d brown	11	£350	18·00	☐ ☐
		12	£750	50·00	☐ ☐

98	9d straw	4	£700	£200	☐ ☐
		5	£10000	*	☐ ☐
112	10d brown	1	£1000	£130	☐ ☐
		2	£12000	£2500	☐ ☐
117	1s green	4	£350	15·00	☐ ☐
		5	£400	12·00	☐ ☐
		6	£550	10·00	☐ ☐
		7	£550	30·00	☐ ☐
119	2s blue	1	£950	60·00	☐ ☐
		3	*	£3000	☐ ☐
126	5s red	1	£2500	£250	☐ ☐
		2	£3500	£325	☐ ☐

Large Coloured Corner Letters (1873–83)

139	2½d mauve	1	£225	25·00	☐ ☐
		2	£225	25·00	☐ ☐
		3	£400	30·00	☐ ☐
141	2½d mauve	3	£500	30·00	☐ ☐
		4	£225	14·00	☐ ☐
		5	£225	18·00	☐ ☐
		6	£225	14·00	☐ ☐
		7	£225	14·00	☐ ☐
		8	£225	18·00	☐ ☐
		9	£225	14·00	☐ ☐
		10	£250	19·00	☐ ☐
		11	£225	14·00	☐ ☐
		12	£225	18·00	☐ ☐
		13	£225	18·00	☐ ☐
		14	£225	14·00	☐ ☐
		15	£225	14·00	☐ ☐
		16	£225	14·00	☐ ☐
		17	£550	90·00	☐ ☐
142	2½d blue	17	£180	20·00	☐ ☐
		18	£200	12·00	☐ ☐
		19	£180	10·00	☐ ☐
		20	£180	10·00	☐ ☐

157	2½d blue	21	£225	9·00	☐
		22	£180	8·00	☐
		23	£180	8·00	☐
143	3d red	11	£200	12·00	☐
		12	£225	14·00	☐
		14	£250	15·00	☐
		15	£200	14·00	☐
		16	£200	14·00	☐
		17	£225	14·00	☐
		18	£225	14·00	☐
		19	£200	14·00	☐
		20	£200	30·00	☐
158	3d red	20	£250	45·00	☐
		21	£200	30·00	☐
152	4d verm	15	£600	£140	☐
		16	*	£10000	☐
153	4d green	15	£450	90·00	☐
		16	£400	85·00	☐
		17	*	£6000	☐
160	4d brown	17	£180	25·00	☐
		18	£180	25·00	☐
147	6d grey	13	£225	22·00	☐
		14	£225	22·00	☐
		15	£225	20·00	☐
		16	£225	20·00	☐
		17	£250	38·00	☐
161	6d grey	17	£180	22·00	☐
		18	£150	22·00	☐
150	1s green	8	£325	35·00	☐
		9	£325	35·00	☐
		10	£300	35·00	☐
		11	£300	35·00	☐
		12	£250	28·00	☐
		13	£250	28·00	☐
		14	*	£10000	☐
163	1s brown	13	£275	45·00	☐
		14	£225	45·00	☐

36

37

38

44   **45**   **46**

47 Small Anchor

48 Orb

Large coloured corner letters

1873–80 (*i*) *Wmk Small Anchor Type* **47**

139	41	2½d mauve *Pl.*	..	£225	25·00	☐ ☐

(*ii*) *Wmk Orb Type* **48**

141	41	2½d mauve *Pl.*		£225	14·00	☐ ☐
142		2½d blue *Pl.*		£180	10·00	☐ ☐

(*iii*) *Wmk Spray of Rose Type* **33**

143	42	3d red *Pl.*	.. ..	£200	12·00	☐ ☐
145	43	6d pale buff (Plate 13)	*	£4500		☐ ☐
147		6d grey *Pl.* ..	..	£225	20·00	☐ ☐
150	44	1s green *Pl.*	.. ..	£250	28·00	☐ ☐
151		1s brown (Plate 13)		£1100	£170	☐ ☐

(*iv*) *Wmk Large Garter Type* **17**

152	45	4d vermilion *Pl.*	..	£600	£140	☐ ☐
153		4d green *Pl.* ..	..	£400	85·00	☐ ☐
154		4d brown (Plate 17)		£600	£140	☐ ☐
156	46	8d orange (Plate 1)		£550	£110	☐ ☐

49 Imperial Crown   **(50)** Surcharges in red **(51)**

3d   6d

41   **42**   **43**

39 Maltese Cross   **40** Large Anchor

1867–83 (*i*) *Wmk Maltese Cross Type* **39**   *Perf* 15½ × 15

126	35	5s red *Pl.*	.. ..	£2500	£250	☐ ☐
128	36	10s grey (Plate 1)	..	£18000	£850	☐ ☐
129	37	£1 brown (Plate 1)		£22000	£1200	☐ ☐

(*ii*) *Wmk Large Anchor Type* **40**   *Perf* 14

134	35	5s red (Plate 4)	..	£4500	£850	☐ ☐
131	36	10s grey (Plate 1)	..	£20000	£1100	☐ ☐
132	37	£1 brown (Plate 1)		£27000	£2000	☐ ☐
137	38	£5 orange (Plate 1)		£4250	£1200	☐ ☐

1880–83 *Wmk Imperial Crown Type* **49**

157	41	2½d blue *Pl.* ..	..	£180	8·00	☐ ☐
158	42	3d red *Pl.* ..	..	£200	30·00	☐ ☐
159		3d on 3d lilac (surch Type **50**)		£225	70·00	☐ ☐
160	45	4d brown *Pl.* ..		£180	25·00	☐ ☐
161	43	6d grey *Pl.* ..	..	£150	22·00	☐ ☐
162		6d on 6d lilac (surch Type **51**)		£200	65·00	☐ ☐
163	44	1s brown *Pl.*	..	£225	45·00	☐ ☐

52

53

54

55

56

1880–81 *Wmk Imperial Crown Type* **49**

164	**52**	½d green	.. ..	15·00	3·00	☐ ☐
166	**53**	1d brown	.. ..	5·00	2·00	☐ ☐
167	**54**	1½d brown	.. ..	80·00	14·00	☐ ☐
168	**55**	2d red ..	.. ..	95·00	30·00	☐ ☐
169	**56**	5d indigo	.. ..	£350	40·00	☐ ☐

57

Die I

Die II

1881 *Wmk Imperial Crown Type* **49**
(*a*) 14 *dots in each corner, Die* I

| 171 | **57** | 1d lilac | .. .. | 75·00 | 12·00 | ☐ ☐ |

(*b*) 16 *dots in each corner, Die* II

| 173 | **57** | 1d lilac | .. .. | 1·00 | 30 | ☐ ☐ |

58

59

60

Coloured letters in the corners

1883-84 *Wmk Anchor Type* **40**

179	**58**	2s 6d deep lilac	.. ..	£200	60·00	☐ ☐
181	**59**	5s red ..	.. ..	£400	75·00	☐ ☐
183	**60**	10s blue..	.. ..	£750	£225	☐ ☐

61

1884 *Wmk* 3 *Imperial Crowns Type* **49**

| 185 | **61** | £1 brown | .. | ..£10000 | £850 | ☐ ☐ |

1888 *Wmk* 3 *Orbs Type* **48**

| 186 | **61** | £1 brown | .. | ..£16000 | £1300 | ☐ ☐ |

1891 *Wmk* 3 *Imperial Crowns Type* **49**

| 212 | **61** | £1 green | .. | .. £2000 | £350 | ☐ ☐ |

62

63

64

65

66

1883–84 *Wmk Imperial Crown Type* **49** (*sideways on horiz. designs*)

187	**52**	½d blue	.. ..	8·00	1·50	☐ ☐
188	**62**	1½d lilac	.. ..	55·00	18·00	☐ ☐
189	**63**	2d lilac	.. ..	70·00	30·00	☐ ☐
190	**64**	2½d lilac	.. ..	40·00	5·00	☐ ☐
191	**65**	3d lilac	.. ..	90·00	40·00	☐ ☐
192	**66**	4d dull green	..	£225	90·00	☐ ☐
193	**62**	5d dull green	..	£225	90·00	☐ ☐
194	**63**	6d dull green	..	£250	95·00	☐ ☐
195	**64**	9d dull green	..	£475	£225	☐ ☐
196	**65**	1s dull green	..	£350	£130	☐ ☐

The above prices are for stamps in the true dull green colour. Stamps which have been soaked, causing the colour to run, are virtually worthless.

67

68

69

70

71

72

73

74

75

76

77

78

KING EDWARD VII
1901 (22 Jan.)–1910 (6 May)

79

80

81

82

83

84

85

86

87

88

89

90

91

92

93

'Jubilee' issue

1887–1900 *The bicoloured stamps have the value tablets,*
or the frames including the value tablets, in the second colour.
Wmk Imperial Crown Type **49**

197	**67**	½d	vermilion	..	1·00	50	☐ ☐
213		½d	green*	.. ..	1·00	60	☐ ☐
198	**68**	1½d	purple and green	10·00	4·00	☐ ☐
200	**69**	2d	green and red	..	15·00	6·00	☐ ☐
201	**70**	2½d	purple on blue	10·00	75	☐ ☐
203	**71**	3d	purple on yellow	15·00	1·50	☐ ☐
205a	**72**	4d	green and brown	18·00	7·25	☐ ☐
206	**73**	4½d	green and red ..	5·00	20·00	☐ ☐
207a	**74**	5d	purple and blue	18·00	6·00	☐ ☐
208	**75**	6d	purple on red ..	18·00	7·50	☐ ☐
209	**76**	9d	purple and blue	40·00	25·00	☐ ☐
210	**77**	10d	purple and red ..	35·00	22·00	☐ ☐
211	**78**	1s	green	£130	30·00	☐ ☐
214		1s	green and red ..	45·00	80·00	☐ ☐
	Set of 14	.. ..	.. .. ..	£325	£190	☐ ☐

* The ½d, No. 213, in blue, has had the colour changed due to exposure
to moisture.

1902–13 *Wmks Imperial Crown Type* **49** (½d to 1s); *Anchor Type* **40** (2s 6d to 10s); *Three Crowns Type* **49** (£1)

    (a) *Perf* 14

215	79	½d	blue-green	..	50	30	□	□
217		½d	yellow-green	..	40	30	□	□
219		1d	red	.. ..	40	30	□	□
288	80	1½d	purple and green		10·00	6·00	□	
291	81	2d	green and red	..	10·00	4·50	□	
231	82	2½d	blue	..	4·00	2·50	□	
232	83	3d	purple on yellow		15·00	2·50	□	
236a	84	4d	green and brown		15·00	7·00	□	
240		4d	orange	.. ..	7·50	6·50	□	
294	85	5d	purple and blue		10·00	4·75	□	
245	79	6d	purple	.. ..	12·00	4·00	□	
249	86	7d	grey	.. ..	3·00	6·00	□	
307	87	9d	purple and blue		30·00	22·00	□	
311	88	10d	purple and red	..	30·00	20·00	□	
314	89	1s	green and red	..	25·00	8·00	□	
260	90	2s 6d	lilac	.. ..	90·00	45·00	□	
263	91	5s	red	.. ..	£100	55·00	□	
319	92	10s	blue	.. ..	£275	£200	□	
320	93	£1	green	.. ..	£750	£300	□	
		Set of 15 *(to* 1s)	.. ..		£160	90·00	□	

    (b) *Perf* 15×14

279a	79	½d	green	.. ..	20·00	20·00	□	□
282		1d	red	.. ..	8·00	3·00	□	□
283	82	2½d	blue	.. ..	10·00	5·00	□	
285	83	3d	purple on yellow		15·00	3·50	□	
286	84	4d	orange	.. ..	10·00	6·00	□	
		Set of 5	.. .. ..		55·00	40·00	□	

KING GEORGE V
1910 (6 May)–1936 (20 Jan.)

PERFORATION. All the following issues are Perf 15×14 except vertical commemorative stamps which are 14×15, unless otherwise stated.

94 (Hair dark)   **95** (Lion unshaded)   **96**

1911–12 *Wmk Imperial Crown Type* **49**

322	94	½d	green	.. ..	2·50	1·00	□	□
327	95	1d	red	.. ..	2·25	1·00	□	□

1912 *Wmk Royal Cypher ('Simple') Type* **96**

335	94	½d	green	.. ..	20·00	22·00	□	□
336	95	1d	red	.. ..	12·00	12·00	□	□

97 (Hair light)   **98** (Lion shaded)   **99**

1912 *Wmk Imperial Crown Type* **49**

339	97	½d	green	.. ..	3·00	50	□
341	98	1d	red ..	.. ..	1·25	50	□

1912 *Wmk Royal Cypher ('Simple') Type* **96**

344	97	½d	green	.. ..	2·50	70	□
345	98	1d	red	.. ..	4·00	50	· □

1912 *Wmk Royal Cypher ('Multiple') Type* **99**

348	97	½d	green	.. ..	6·00	4·00	□
350	98	1d	red	.. ..	5·00	4·50	□

100   **101**   **102**

103   **104**

1912–24 *Wmk Royal Cypher Type* **96**

351	101	½d	green	.. ..	30	25	□
357	100	1d	red ..	.. ..	30	25	□
362	101	1½d	brown	.. ..	1·00	25	□
368	102	2d	orange	.. ..	1·00	50	□
372	100	2½d	blue	.. ..	4·50	1·00	□
375	102	3d	violet	.. ..	2·00	75	□
379		4d	grey-green	..	4·00	75	□
381	103	5d	brown	.. ..	3·50	3·00	□
385		6d	purple	.. ..	6·00	1·50	□
			a. *Perf* 14	..	60·00	85·00	□
387		7d	olive-green	..	6·00	3·75	□
390		8d	black on yellow		15·00	6·50	□
392	104	9d	black	.. ..	5·00	2·25	□
393a		9d	olive-green	..	65·00	15·00	□
394		10d	blue	.. ..	9·00	12·00	□
395		1s	brown	.. ..	7·50	1·00	□
		Set of 15	.. .. ..		£120	45·00	□

| 97 | **101** | ½d green | .. | .. | 50·00 | 95·00 | ☐ ☐ |
| 98 | **100** | 1d red .. | .. | ... | £110 | £130 | ☐ ☐ |

ee also Nos. 418/29.

105

106

105. Background around portrait consists of horizontal lines

913–18 *Wmk Single Cypher Type* **106**   *Perf* 11 × 12

13a	**105**	2s 6d brown	..		70·00	25·00	☐ ☐
16		5s red ..	..	..	£125	45·00	☐ ☐
17		10s blue		..	£175	80·00	☐ ☐
03		£1 green	..	..	£950	£600	☐ ☐
	Set of 4	..	..	..	£1200	£700	☐ ☐

ee also Nos. 450/2.

107

924–26 *Wmk Block Cypher Type* **107**

18	**101**	½d green	..	..	15	25	☐ ☐
19	**100**	1d red ..	..	..	15	25	☐ ☐
20	**101**	1½d brown	..	..	15	25	☐ ☐
21	**102**	2d orange	..	..	75	80	☐ ☐
22	**100**	2½d blue	..	..	3·00	1·25	☐ ☐
23	**102**	3d violet	..	..	4·00	1·00	☐ ☐
24		4d grey-green	..		6·00	1·00	☐ ☐
25	**103**	5d brown	..	..	10·00	1·60	☐ ☐
26a		6d purple	..	..	1·50	50	☐ ☐
27	**104**	9d olive-green	..		5·00	2·25	☐ ☐
28		10d blue	..	..	15·00	16·00	☐ ☐
29		1s brown	..	..	10·00	1·00	☐ ☐
	Set of 12	..	..	..	50·00	23·00	☐ ☐

or full information on all future British issues, collectors
hould write to the British Post Office Philatelic Bureau, 20
randon Street, Edinburgh EH3 5TT

108   **109**

British Empire Exhibition

1924–25 *Wmk* **107**   *Perf* 14

(*a*) 23.4.24.   *Dated '1924'*

430	**108**	1d red ..	..	..	5·00	6·00	☐ ☐
431	**109**	1½d brown	..		7·50	11·00	☐ ☐
	First Day Cover	..	..'	..		£350	☐

(*b*) 9.5.25.   *Dated '1925'*

432	**108**	1d red ..	..	..	8·00	17·00	☐ ☐
433	**109**	1½d brown	..		25·00	50·00	☐ ☐
	First Day Cover	..	..	..		£1200	☐

110   **111**   **112**

113 St George and the Dragon

114

9

Ninth Universal Postal Union Congress

1929 (10 MAY) (a) *Wmk* **107**

434	110	½d green	..	..	1·50	1·50	□ □
435	111	1d red	..	..	1·50	1·50	□ □
436		1½d brown	..	..	1·00	1·00	□ □
437	112	2½d blue	..	..	7·50	9·00	□ □
	(b) *Wmk* **114** *Perf* 12						
438	113	£1 black	..	..	£500	£400	□ □
434/7 *Set of 4*			..	..	10·00	11·50	□ □
434/7 *First Day Cover* (4 *vals.*)					£500	□
434/8 *First Day Cover* (5 *vals.*)			..		£2500	□

115

116

117

118

119

1934–36 *Wmk* **107**

439	115	½d green	..	..	10	25	□ □
440	116	1d red	..	..	10	25	□ □
441	115	1½d brown	..	..	10	25	□ □
442	117	2d orange	..	..	25	25	□ □
443	116	2½d blue	..	..	75	60	□ □
444	117	3d violet	..	..	75	50	□ □
445		4d grey-green	..	..	1·00	55	□ □
446	118	5d brown	..	..	3·50	1·50	□ □
447	119	9d olive-green	..	6·00	1·60	□ □
448		10d blue	..	..	6·00	8·00	□ □
449		1s brown	..	..	8·00	50	□ □
	Set of 11		..	..	24·00	11·00	□ □

T 105 (re-engraved). *Background around portrait consists of horizontal and diagonal lines*

1934 *Wmk* **106** *Perf* 11 × 12

450	105	2s 6d brown	..	..	40·00	15·00	□ □
451		5s red	..	..	85·00	40·00	□ □
452		10s blue	..	..	£200	40·00	□ □
	Set of 3		..	..	£275	85·00	□ □

120

121

122

123

Silver Jubilee

1935 (7 MAY) *Wmk* **107**

453	120	½d green	..	..	75	20	□ □
454	121	1d red	..	..	1·00	1·00	□ □
455	122	1½d brown	..	..	75	20	□ □
456	123	2½d blue	..	..	3·00	5·50	□ □
	Set of 4		..	..	5·00	6·00	□ □
	First Day Cover	..	..		£400	□

KING EDWARD VIII
1936 (20 Jan.–10 Dec.)

124

125

1936 *Wmk* **125**

457	124	½d green	..	..	20	15	□ □
458		1d red	..	..	50	20	□ □
459		1½d brown	..	..	25	15	□ □
460		2½d blue	..	..	25	60	□ □
	Set of 4		..	..	1·00	1·00	□ □

10

26 King George VI
and Queen Elizabeth

131 King George VI

131a

132

132a

127

133

Coronation

1937 (13 MAY) Wmk 127

461	126	1½d brown	.. ..	40	25	☐	☐
		First Day Cover	.. .. ..		28·00		☐

128

129

130

King George VI and National Emblems

1937–47 Wmk 127

462	128	½d green	.. ..	10	15	☐ ☐
463		1d scarlet	.. ..	10	15	☐ ☐
464		1½d brown	.. ..	20	15	☐ ☐
465		2d orange	.. ..	1·25	45	☐ ☐
466		2½d blue	.. ..	25	15	☐ ☐
467		3d violet	.. ..	6·00	60	☐ ☐
468	129	4d green	.. ..	35	40	☐ ☐
469		5d brown	.. ..	2·50	35	☐ ☐
470		6d purple	.. ..	1·75	40	☐ ☐
471	130	7d green	.. ..	5·00	50	☐ ☐
472		8d red	.. ..	5·00	50	☐ ☐
473		9d deep green	..	6·50	50	☐ ☐
474		10d blue	.. ..	6·50	60	☐ ☐
474a		11d plum	.. ..	3·00	1·50	☐ ☐
475		1s brown	.. ..	7·50	40	☐ ☐
		Set of 15	.. ..	42·00	6·00	☐ ☐

For later printings of the lower values in apparently lighter shades and different colours, see Nos. 485/90 and 503/8.

For full information on all future British issues, collectors should write to the British Post Office Philatelic Bureau, 20 Brandon Street, Edinburgh EH3 5TT.

1939–48 Wmk 133 Perf 14

476	131	2s 6d brown	.. ..	40·00	7·00	☐ ☐
476a		2s 6d green	.. ..	9·00	1·00	☐ ☐
477	131a	5s red	.. ..	18·00	1·50	☐ ☐
478	132	10s dark blue	..	£130	18·00	☐ ☐
478a		10s bright blue	..	40·00	4·50	☐ ☐
478b	132a	£1 brown	.. ..	15·00	19·00	☐ ☐
		Set of 6	.. ..	£225	45·00	☐ ☐

134 Queen Victoria and King George VI

Centenary of First Adhesive Postage Stamps

1940 (6 MAY) Wmk 127 Perf 14½×14

479	134	½d green	.. ..	30	20	☐ ☐
480		1d red	.. ..	90	40	☐ ☐
481		1½d brown	.. ..	30	30	☐ ☐
482		2d orange	.. ..	50	40	☐ ☐
483		2½d blue	.. ..	1·90	80	☐ ☐
484		3d violet	.. ..	4·00	4·00	☐ ☐
		Set of 6	.. ..	7·00	5·50	☐ ☐
		First Day Cover	.. ..		35·00	☐

Head as Nos. 462/7, but lighter background

1941–42 *Wmk* **127**

485	**128**	½d pale green	..	15	10	☐	☐
486		1d pale red	..	15	10	☐	☐
487		1½d pale brown	..	75	45	☐	☐
488		2d pale orange	..	50	40	☐	☐
489		2½d light blue	..	15	10	☐	☐
490		3d pale violet	..	1·50	50	☐	☐
	Set of 6	.. .. ..	..	2·75	1·50	☐	☐

135 Symbols of Peace and Reconstruction

136 Symbols of Peace and Reconstruction

Victory

1946 (11 JUNE) *Wmk* **127**

491	**135**	2½d blue	.. ..	25	15	☐	☐
492	**136**	3d violet	.. ..	25	15	☐	☐
	First Day Cover	.. .. ..		48·00		☐	

137 King George VI and Queen Elizabeth

138 King George VI and Queen Elizabeth

Royal Silver Wedding

1948 (26 APR.) *Wmk* **127**

493	**137**	2½d blue	.. ..	30	30	☐	☐
494	**138**	£1 blue	.. ..	32·00	32·00	☐	☐
	First Day Cover	.. ..		£375		☐	

1948 (10 MAY)

Stamps of 1d and 2½d showing seaweed-gathering were on sale at eight Head Post Offices elsewhere in Great Britain, but were primarily for use in the Channel Islands and are listed there (see after Regional Issues).

139 Globe and Laurel Wreath

140 'Speed'

141 Olympic Symbol

142 Winged Victory

Olympic Games

1948 (29 JULY) *Wmk* **127**

495	**139**	2½d blue	.. ..	10	10	☐	☐
496	**140**	3d violet	.. ..	30	30	☐	☐
497	**141**	6d purple	.. ..	60	30	☐	☐
498	**142**	1s brown	.. ..	1·25	1·50	☐	☐
	Set of 4	.. ..	..	2·00	2·00	☐	☐
	First Day Cover	.. ..		35·00		☐	

143 Two Hemispheres

144 U.P.U. Monument, Berne

145 Goddess Concordia, Globe and Points of Compass

146 Posthorn and Globe

75th Anniversary of Universal Postal Union

1949 (10 OCT.) *Wmk* **127**

499	**143**	2½d blue	.. ..	10	10	☐	☐
500	**144**	3d violet	.. ..	30	40	☐	☐
501	**145**	6d purple	.. ..	60	75	☐	☐
502	**146**	1s brown	.. ..	1·25	1·50	☐	☐
	Set of 4	.. ..		2·00	2·75	☐	☐
	First Day Cover	.. ..		60·00		☐	☐

4d as No. 468 and others as Nos. 485/9, but colours changed

1950–52 *Wmk* **127**

603	**128**	½d pale orange	..	10	15	☐	☐
604		1d light blue	..	15	15	☐	☐
605		1½d pale green	..	25	30	☐	☐
606		2d pale brown	..	25	20	☐	☐
607		2½d pale red	..	20	15	☐	☐
608	**129**	4d light blue	..	1·50	1·10	☐	☐
	Set of 6	.. .. ..		2·25	1·75	☐	☐

147 HMS *Victory*

148 White Cliffs of Dover

149 St George and the Dragon

150 Royal Coat of Arms

1951 (3 MAY) *Wmk* **133** *Perf* 11×12

509	**147**	2s 6d green	.. ..	8·00	75	☐	☐
510	**148**	5s red	.. .. ..	30·00	1·50	☐	☐
511	**149**	10s blue	.. ..	18·00	10·00	☐	☐
512	**150**	£1 brown	.. ..	40·00	14·00	☐	☐
	Set of 4	.. .. ..		85·00	24·00	☐	☐

151 Commerce and Prosperity

152 Festival Symbol

Festival of Britain

1951 (3 MAY) *Wmk* **127**

513	**151**	2½d red	.. ..	25	15	☐	☐
514	**152**	4d blue	.. ..	50	45	☐	☐
	First Day Cover	.. ..			20·00		☐

QUEEN ELIZABETH II
6 February, 1952

153 Tudor Crown

154

155

156

157

158

159

160

Queen Elizabeth II and National Emblems

1952–54 *Wmk* **153**

515	**154**	½d orange	.. ..	10	15	☐	☐
516		1d blue	.. ..	20	20	☐	☐
517		1½d green	.. ..	10	15	☐	☐
518		2d brown	.. ..	20	15	☐	☐
519	**155**	2½d red	.. ..	10	15	☐	☐
520		3d lilac	.. ..	1·00	30	☐	☐
521	**156**	4d blue	.. ..	3·00	80	☐	☐
		4½d (*See Nos.* 577, 594, 609 *and* 616*b*)					
522	**157**	5d brown	.. ..	90	2·00	☐	☐
523		6d purple	.. ..	3·00	60	☐	☐
524		7d green	.. ..	10·00	3·50	☐	☐
525	**158**	8d magenta	.. ..	1·00	60	☐	☐
526		9d bronze-green	..	22·00	3·00	☐	☐
527		10d blue	.. ..	18·00	3·00	☐	☐
528		11d plum	.. ..	35·00	16·00	☐	☐
529	**159**	1s bistre	.. ..	1·00	40	☐	☐
530	**160**	1s 3d green	.. ..	5·00	2·00	☐	☐
531	**159**	1s 6d indigo	.. ..	12·00	2·75	☐	☐
	Set of 17	.. .. ..		£100	28·00	☐	☐

See also Nos. 540/56, 561/6, 570/94 and 599/618*a*.
For First Day Cover prices see page 36.

161

162

163

164

Coronation

1953 (3 JUNE) *Wmk* **153**

532	**161**	2½d red	..			10	50	☐ ☐
533	**162**	4d blue				30	1·00	☐ ☐
534	**163**	1s 3d green				4·00	3·00	☐ ☐
535	**164**	1s 6d blue	..			6·75	7·00	☐ ☐
		Set of 4	..	..	..	10·00	10·00	☐ ☐
		First Day Cover	..	..			40·00	☐

165 St Edward's Crown

166 Carrickfergus Castle

167 Caernarvon Castle

168 Edinburgh Castle

169 Windsor Castle

1955–58 *Wmk* **165**   *Perf* 11 × 12

536	**166**	2s 6d brown				10·00	2·00	☐ ☐
537	**167**	5s red	..			40·00	3·50	☐ ☐
538	**168**	10s blue		..		95·00	11·00	☐ ☐
539	**169**	£1 black		..		£160	28·00	☐ ☐
		Set of 4	..	..		£275	40·00	☐ ☐

See also Nos. 595*a*/8*a*, 759/62 and F.D.C's on page 36.

1955–58 *Wmk* **165**

540	**154**	½d orange	..	..	10	15	☐
541		1d blue	..	..	25	15	☐
542		1½d green	..		10	15	☐
543		2d red-brown	..		20	20	☐
543*b*		2d light red-brown		20	15	☐
544	**155**	2½d red	..	..	20	15	☐
545		3d lilac	..	..	20	15	☐
546	**156**	4d blue	..	..	1·40	40	☐
547	**157**	5d brown	..	..	4·00	3·50	☐
548*a*		6d purple	..	..	3·50	80	☐
549		7d green	..	..	48·00	7·50	☐
550	**158**	8d magenta	..		5·50	1·00	☐
551		9d bronze-green	..	17·00	2·25	☐
552		10d blue	..	..	12·00	2·25	☐
553		11d plum	..	..	40	1·50	☐
554	**159**	1s bistre	..	..	15·00	40	☐
555	**160**	1s 3d green	..		17·00	1·50	☐
556	**159**	1s 6d indigo	..		16·00	1·25	☐
		Set of 18	..	..	£120	22·00	☐

170 Scout Badge and 'Rolling Hitch'

171 'Scouts coming to Britain'

172 Globe within a Compass

173

World Scout Jubilee Jamboree

1957 (1 AUG.) *Wmk* **165**

557	**170**	2½d red	..	..		15	10	☐ ☐
558	**171**	4d blue	..	..		50	1·00	☐ ☐
559	**172**	1s 3d green	..	..		5·00	4·50	☐ ☐
		Set of 3	..	..		5·00	5·00	☐ ☐
		First Day Cover	..	..			15·00	☐

46th Inter Parliamentary Union Conference

1957 (12 SEPT.) *Wmk* **165**

560	**173**	4d blue	..	..	1·10	1·10	☐
		First Day Cover	..	..		95·00	☐

Graphite-lined and Phosphor Issues

These are used in connection with automatic sorting machinery, originally experimentally at Southampton but now also operating elsewhere. In such areas these stamps were the normal issue, but from mid 1967 *all* low-value stamps bear phosphor markings.

The graphite lines were printed in black on the back, beneath the gum; two lines per stamp except for the 2d (*see below*).

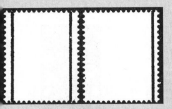

174   **175** (2d only)

(Stamps viewed from back)

In November 1959, phosphor bands, printed on the front, replaced the graphite. They are wider than the graphite, not easy to see, but show as broad vertical bands at certain angles to the light.

Values representing the rate for printed papers (and second class mail from 1968) have one band and others have two, three or four bands according to size and format. From 1972 onwards some commemorative stamps were printed with 'all-over' phosphor.

In the small stamps the bands are on each side with the single band at left (except where otherwise stated). In the large-size commemorative stamps the single band may be at left, centre or right varying in different issues. The bands are vertical on both horizontal and vertical designs except where otherwise stated.

See also notes on page 35.

Graphite-lined issue

1957 (19 Nov.) *Two graphite lines on the back, except 2d value, which has one line. Wmk* **165**

561	**154**	½d orange	..	..	20	30	□	□
562		1d blue	..	..	20	35	□	□
563		1½d green	..	..	40	1·25	□	□
564		2d light red-brown		..	3·00	1·50	□	□
565	**155**	2½d red	..	..	7·00	8·00	□	□
566		3d lilac	..	..	50	50	□	□
	Set of 6	..	..	..	10·00	11·00	□	□

See also Nos. 587/94.

For First Day Cover price see page 36.

176 Welsh Dragon

177 Flag and Games Emblem

178 Welsh Dragon

Sixth British Empire and Commonwealth Games, Cardiff

1958 (18 July) *Wmk* **165**

567	**176**	3d lilac	..	..	15	10	□	□
568	**177**	6d mauve	..	..	25	50	□	□
569	**178**	1s 3d green	..	..	2·75	2·50	□	□
	Set of 3	..	..	..	2·75	2·75	□	□
	First Day Cover	..	..	..		55·00		□

179 Multiple Crowns

WATERMARK. All the following issues to No. 755 are Watermark **179** (sideways on the vertical commemorative stamps) unless otherwise stated.

1958–65 *Wmk* **179**

570	**154**	½d orange	..	..	10	10	□	□
571		1d blue	..	..	10	10	□	□
572		1½d green	..	..	10	15	□	□
573		2d light red-brown		..	10	10	□	□
574	**155**	2½d red	..	..	10	10	□	□
575		3d lilac	..	..	10	10	□	□
576a	**156**	4d blue	..	..	15	10	□	□
577		4½d brown	..	..	10	15	□	□
578	**157**	5d brown	..	..	25	20	□	□
579		6d purple	..	..	25	15	□	□
580		7d green	..	..	40	20	□	□
581	**158**	8d magenta	..	..	40	15	□	□
582		9d bronze-green	..		40	15	□	□
583		10d blue	..	..	1·00	15	□	□
584	**159**	1s bistre	..	..	40	15	□	□
585	**160**	1s 3d green	..	..	25	15	□	□
586	**159**	1s 6d indigo	..	..	6·00	40	□	□
	Set of 17	..	..	..	9·00	2·10	□	□

For 4½d on First Day Cover see page 36.

For full information on all future British issues, collectors should write to the British Post Office Philatelic Bureau, 20 Brandon Street, Edinburgh EH3 5TT

Graphite-lined issue

1958–61 *Two graphite lines on the back, except 2d value, which has one line.* **Wmk 179**

587	154	½d orange	.. ..	6·00	6·00	☐ ☐
588		1d blue	.. ..	1·00	1·50	☐ ☐
589		1½d green	.. ..	40·00	40·00	☐ ☐
590		2d light red-brown		7·00	3·25	☐ ☐
591	155	2½d red	.. ..	12·00	10·00	☐ ☐
592		3d lilac	.. ..	50	50	☐ ☐
593	156	4d blue	.. ..	4·00	4·50	☐ ☐
594		4½d brown	.. ..	5·00	4·50	☐ ☐
		Set of 8	.. ..	65·00	60·00	☐ ☐

The prices quoted for No. 589 are for examples with inverted watermark. Stamps with upright watermark are *priced at £85 mint, £60 used.*

1959–63 *Wmk* **179**   *Perf* 11 × 12

595a	166	2s 6d brown	.. ..	50	30	☐ ☐
596a	167	5s red	.. ..	1·00	60	☐ ☐
597a	168	10s blue	.. ..	2·50	3·00	☐ ☐
598a	169	£1 black	.. ..	10·00	5·00	☐ ☐
		Set of 4	.. ..	13·00	8·00	☐ ☐

Phosphor-Graphite issue

1959 (18 Nov.) *Two phosphor bands on front and two graphite lines on back, except 2d value, which has one band on front and one line on back*

(a) Wmk **165**

599	154	½d orange	.. ..	4·00	6·00	☐ ☐
600		1d blue	.. ..	6·00	6·00	☐ ☐
601		1½d green	.. ..	2·50	5·00	☐ ☐

(b) Wmk **179**

605	154	2d light red-brown (1 band) ..		5·00	3·75	☐ ☐
606	155	2½d red	.. ..	22·00	11·00	☐ ☐
607		3d lilac	.. ..	11·00	8·00	☐ ☐
608	156	4d blue	.. ..	12·00	25·00	☐ ☐
609		4½d brown	.. ..	28·00	15·00	☐ ☐
		Set of 8	.. ..	80·00	70·00	☐ ☐

Phosphor issue

1960–67 *Two phosphor bands on front, except where otherwise stated.* Wmk **179**

610	154	½d orange	.. ..	10	15	☐ ☐
611		1d blue	.. ..	10	10	☐ ☐
612		1½d green	.. ..	10	20	☐ ☐
613		2d light red-brown (1 band)		22·00	20·00	☐ ☐
613a		2d light red-brown (2 bands)		10	10	☐ ☐
614	155	2½d red (2 bands) ..		10	40	☐ ☐
614a		2½d red (1 band)	..	40	75	☐ ☐
615		3d lilac (2 bands)		60	45	☐ ☐
615c		3d lilac (1 side band)		35	60	☐ ☐
615e		3d lilac (1 centre band)		25	40	☐ ☐
616a	156	4d blue	.. ..	15	15	☐ ☐
616b		4½d brown	..	15	25	☐ ☐
616c	157	5d brown	.. ..	20	25	☐ ☐
617		6d purple	.. ..	40	20	☐ ☐
617a		7d green	.. ..	60	25	☐ ☐
617b	158	8d magenta ..		20	25	☐ ☐
617c		9d bronze-green	..	60	25	☐ ☐
617d		10d blue	.. ..	80	35	☐ ☐
617e	159	1s bistre	.. ..	40	20	☐ ☐
618	160	1s 3d green	.. ..	1·75	2·50	☐ ☐
618a	159	1s 6d indigo	.. ..	2·00	1·00	☐ ☐
		Set of 17 (one of each value)		7·00	6·00	☐ ☐

No. 615c exists with the phosphor band at the left or right of the stamp.

180 Postboy of 1660   **181** Posthorn of 1660

Tercentenary of Establishment of 'General Letter Office'

1960 (7 July)

619	180	3d lilac	.. ..	20	10	☐ ☐
620	181	1s 3d green	.. ..	4·50	4·25	☐ ☐
		Set of 2	.. ..	4·50	4·25	☐ ☐
		First Day Cover ..	.. ..		45·00	☐

182 Conference Emblem

First Anniversary of European Postal and Telecommunications Conference

1960 (19 Sept.)

621	182	6d green and purple		40	60	☐ ☐
622		1s 6d brown and blue		6·50	5·50	☐ ☐
		Set of 2	.. ..	6·50	5·50	☐ ☐
		First Day Cover ..	.. ..		30·00	☐

183 Thrift Plant   **184** 'Growth of Savings'

185 Thrift Plant

Centenary of Post Office Savings Bank

1961 (28 Aug.)

623	183	2½d black and red ..	10	10	☐	☐
624	184	3d orange-brown and violet ..	10	10	☐	☐
625	185	1s 6d red and blue ..	2·50	2·00	☐	☐
		Set of 3	2·50	2·00	☐	☐
		First Day Cover		60·00		☐

186 C.E.P.T. Emblem

187 Doves and Emblem

188 Doves and Emblem

European Postal and Telecommunications (C.E.P.T.) Conference, Torquay

1961 (18 Sept.)

626	186	2d orange, pink and brown ..	10	10	☐	☐
627	187	4d buff, mauve and ultramarine ..	20	10	☐	☐
628	188	10d turquoise, green and blue	40	25	☐	☐
		Set of 3	60	40	☐	☐
		First Day Cover		2·50		☐

189 Hammer Beam Roof, Westminster Hall

190 Palace of Westminster

Seventh Commonwealth Parliamentary Conference

1961 (25 Sept.)

629	189	6d purple and gold	25	20	☐	☐
630	190	1s 3d green and blue	2·75	2·00	☐	☐
		Set of 2	3·00	2·10	☐	☐
		First Day Cover		26·00		☐

191 'Units of Productivity'

192 'National Productivity'

193 'Unified Productivity'

National Productivity Year

1962 (14 Nov.) Wmk **179** (inverted on 2½d and 3d)

631	191	2½d green and red ..	20	10	☐	☐
		p. Phosphor ..	1·00	40	☐	☐
632	192	3d blue and violet ..	25	10	☐	☐
		p. Phosphor ..	1·00	50	☐	☐
633	193	1s 3d red, blue and green	2·50	1·60	☐	☐
		p. Phosphor	24·00	21·00	☐	☐
		Set of 3 (Ordinary)	2·75	1·60	☐	☐
		Set of 3 (Phosphor)	24·00	21·00	☐	☐
		First Day Cover (Ordinary) ..		35·00		☐
		First Day Cover (Phosphor)		95·00		☐

194 Campaign Emblem and Family

195 Children of Three Races

Freedom from Hunger

1963 (21 Mar.) Wmk **179** (inverted)

634	194	2½d crimson and pink	10	10	☐	☐
		p. Phosphor ..	1·00	1·00	☐	☐
635	195	1s 3d brown and yellow	2·75	2·50	☐	☐
		p. Phosphor ..	24·00	22·00	☐	☐
		Set of 2 (Ordinary)	2·75	2·50	☐	☐
		Set of 2 (Phosphor)	24·00	23·00	☐	☐
		First Day Cover (Ordinary) ..		28·00		☐
		First Day Cover (Phosphor)..		30·00		☐

196 'Paris Conference'

Paris Postal Conference Centenary

1963 (7 MAY) *Wmk 179 (inverted)*

636	**196**	6d green and mauve	60	40	☐	☐
		p. Phosphor ..	6·50	6·50	☐	☐
		First Day Cover (Ordinary) ..		15·00		☐
		First Day Cover (Phosphor) ..		25·00		☐

197 Posy of Flowers

198 Woodland Life

National Nature Week

1963 (16 MAY)

637	**197**	3d multicoloured ..	20	20	☐	☐
		p. Phosphor ..	50	50	☐	☐
638	**198**	4½d multicoloured ..	40	40	☐	☐
		p. Phosphor ..	3·50	3·00	☐	☐
		Set of 2 (Ordinary) ..	60	60	☐	☐
		Set of 2 (Phosphor) ..	4·00	3·50	☐	☐
		First Day Cover (Ordinary) ..		16·00		☐
		First Day Cover (Phosphor)		30·00		☐

199 Rescue at Sea

200 19th-century Lifeboat

201 Lifeboatmen

Ninth International Lifeboat Conference, Edinburgh

1963 (31 MAY)

639	**199**	2½d blue, black and red	10	10	☐	☐
		p. Phosphor ..	40	50	☐	☐
640	**200**	4d multicoloured ..	40	30	☐	☐
		p. Phosphor ..	20	50	☐	☐
641	**201**	1s 6d sepia, yellow and blue	4·50	4·00	☐	☐
		p. Phosphor ..	32·00	28·00	☐	☐
		Set of 3 (Ordinary)	4·50	4·00	☐	☐
		Set of 3 (Phosphor)	32·00	28·00	☐	☐
		First Day Cover (Ordinary) ..		30·00		☐
		First Day Cover (Phosphor) ..		40·00		☐

202 Red Cross

203

204

205 'Commonwealth Cable'

Red Cross Centenary Congress

1963 (15 AUG.)

642	**202**	3d red and lilac ..	10	10	☐	☐
		p. Phosphor ..	60	60	☐	☐
643	**203**	1s 3d red, blue and grey	3·25	2·75	☐	☐
		p. Phosphor ..	35·00	35·00	☐	☐
644	**204**	1s 6d red, blue and bistre ..	3·25	2·75	☐	☐
		p. Phosphor ..	26·00	20·00	☐	☐
		Set of 3 (Ordinary) ..	6·00	5·00	☐	☐
		Set of 3 (Phosphor) ..	55·00	50·00	☐	☐
		First Day Cover (Ordinary) ..		35·00		☐
		First Day Cover (Phosphor)		65·00		☐

Opening of COMPAC (Trans-Pacific Telephone Cable)

1963 (3 DEC.)

645	**205**	1s 6d blue and black	3·25	3·25	☐	☐
		p. Phosphor ..	18·00	20·00	☐	☐
		First Day Cover (Ordinary) ..		25·00		☐
		First Day Cover (Phosphor) ..		30·00		☐

06 Puck and Bottom
(*A Midsummer Night's Dream*)

207 Feste (*Twelfth Night*)

08 Balcony Scene
(*Romeo and Juliet*)

209 'Eve of Agincourt'
(*Henry V*)

210 Hamlet contemplating Yorick's skull (*Hamlet*) and Queen Elizabeth II

Shakespeare Festival

964 (23 APR.)   *Perf 11 × 12 (2s 6d) or 15 × 14 (others)*.

46	**206**	3d bis, blk & vio-bl	10	10	☐	☐
		p. Phosphor ..	20	30	☐	☐
47	**207**	6d multicoloured ..	20	20	☐	☐
		p. Phosphor ..	60	70	☐	☐
48	**208**	1s 3d multicoloured ..	1·00	1·25	☐	☐
		p. Phosphor ..	5·75	7·25	☐	☐
49	**209**	1s 6d multicoloured ..	1·25	1·25	☐	☐
		p. Phosphor ..	11·00	7·25	☐	☐
50	**210**	2s 6d deep slate-purple	2·00	2·00	☐	☐
		Set of 5 (Ordinary) ..	4·25	4·25	☐	☐
		Set of 4 (Phosphor) ..	15·00	14·00	☐	☐
		First Day Cover (Ordinary)		11·00		☐
		First Day Cover (Phosphor)		12·00		☐
		Presentation Pack (Ordinary) 12·00			☐	

RESENTATION PACKS were first introduced by the P.O. for the Shakespeare Festival issue. The packs include he set of stamps and details of the designs, the designer nd the stamp printer. They were issued for almost all later efinitive and special issues.

For note about Presentation Packs in foreign languages, e page 25.

11 Flats near Richmond Park
('Urban Development')

212 Shipbuilding Yards, Belfast
('Industrial Activity')

213 Beddgelert Forest Park, Snowdonia ('Forestry')

214 Nuclear Reactor, Dounreay ('Technological Development')

20th International Geographical Congress, London

1964 (1 JULY)

651	**211**	2½d multicoloured ..	10	10	☐	☐
		p. Phosphor ..	50	40	☐	☐
652	**212**	4d multicoloured ..	25	25	☐	☐
		p. Phosphor ..	90	70	☐	☐
653	**213**	8d multicoloured ..	50	50	☐	☐
		p. Phosphor ..	2·00	1·75	☐	☐
654	**214**	1s 6d multicoloured ..	4·00	3·75	☐	☐
		p. Phosphor ..	24·00	24·00	☐	☐
		Set of 4 (Ordinary) ..	4·50	4·25	☐	☐
		Set of 4 (Phosphor) ..	24·00	24·00	☐	☐
		First Day Cover (Ordinary) ..		18·00		☐
		First Day Cover (Phosphor)		30·00		☐
		Presentation Pack (Ordinary) 90·00			☐	

215 Spring Gentian

216 Dog Rose

217 Honeysuckle

218 Fringed Water Lily

Tenth International Botanical Congress, Edinburgh

1964 (5 AUG.)

655	**215**	3d vio. blue & green	10	10	☐	☐
		p. Phosphor ..	20	20	☐	☐
656	**216**	6d multicoloured ..	20	20	☐	☐
		p. Phosphor ..	1·25	1·40	☐	☐
657	**217**	9d multicoloured ..	2·25	2·25	☐	☐
		p. Phosphor ..	3·75	5·00	☐	☐
658	**218**	1s 3d multicoloured ..	3·00	2·10	☐	☐
		p. Phosphor ..	22·00	22·00	☐	☐
		Set of 4 (Ordinary) ..	5·00	4·25	☐	☐
		Set of 4 (Phosphor) ..	24·00	24·00	☐	☐
		First Day Cover (Ordinary) ..		18·00		☐
		First Day Cover (Phosphor)		32·00		☐
		Presentation Pack (Ordinary) 90·00			☐	

219 Forth Road Bridge **220** Forth Road and Railway Bridges

Opening of Forth Road Bridge

1964 (4 Sept.)

659	**219**	3d black, blue and violet	15	10	☐	☐
		p. Phosphor	50	50	☐	☐
660	**220**	6d black, blue and red	45	40	☐	☐
		p. Phosphor	5·00	5·50	☐	☐
		Set of 2 (Ordinary)	60	50	☐	☐
		Set of 2 (Phosphor)	5·50	6·00	☐	☐
		First Day Cover (Ordinary)		6·00		☐
		First Day Cover (Phosphor)		12·00		☐
		Presentation Pack (Ordinary)	£200			☐

221 Sir Winston Churchill **222** Sir Winston Churchill

Churchill Commemoration

1965 (8 July)

661	**221**	4d black and drab	15	10	☐	☐
		p. Phosphor	30	30	☐	☐
662	**222**	1s 3d black and grey	45	30	☐	☐
		p. Phosphor	3·00	3·50	☐	☐
		Set of 2 (Ordinary)	60	40	☐	☐
		Set of 2 (Phosphor)	3·25	3·75	☐	☐
		First Day Cover (Ordinary)		2·00		☐
		First Day Cover (Phosphor)		4·50		☐
		Presentation Pack (Ordinary)	13·00			☐

223 Simon de Montfort's Seal

224 Parliament Buildings (after engraving by Hollar, 1647)

700th Anniversary of Simon de Montfort's Parliament

1965 (19 July)

663	**223**	6d green	10	10	☐	
		p. Phosphor	40	40	☐	
664	**224**	2s 6d black, grey and drab	1·25	1·25	☐	
		Set of 2 (Ordinary)	1·25	1·25	☐	
		First Day Cover (Ordinary)		12·00		
		First Day Cover (Phosphor)		16·00		
		Presentation Pack (Ordinary)	35·00		☐	

225 Bandsmen and Banner

226 Three Salvationists

Salvation Army Centenary

1965 (9 Aug.)

665	**225**	3d multicoloured	10	10	☐	
		p. Phosphor	40	40	☐	
666	**226**	1s 6d multicoloured	1·00	1·00	☐	
		p. Phosphor	3·50	4·25	☐	
		Set of 2 (Ordinary)	1·10	1·10	☐	
		Set of 2 (Phosphor)	3·75	4·25	☐	
		First Day Cover (Ordinary)		24·00		
		First Day Cover (Phosphor)		24·00		

227 Lister's Carbolic Spray **228** Lister and Chemical Symbols

Centenary of Joseph Lister's Discovery of Antiseptic Surgery

1965 (1 Sept.)

667	**227**	4d indigo, chestnut and grey	10	10	☐	
		p. Phosphor	15	20	☐	
668	**228**	1s black, purple and blue			☐	
			1·00	1·25	☐	
		p. Phosphor	1·60	1·60	☐	
		Set of 2 (Ordinary)	1·10	1·25	☐	
		Set of 2 (Phosphor)	1·75	1·75	☐	
		First Day Cover (Ordinary)		9·00		
		First Day Cover (Phosphor)		10·00		

29 Trinidad Carnival Dancers   230 Canadian Folk-dancers

Commonwealth Arts Festival
1965 (1 SEPT.)

69	229	6d black and orange	10	10	☐	☐
		p. Phosphor	30	30	☐	☐
70	230	1s 6d black and violet	1·40	1·40	☐	☐
		p. Phosphor	2·25	2·25	☐	☐
		Set of 2 (Ordinary)	1·50	1·50	☐	☐
		Set of 2 (Phosphor)	2·50	2·50	☐	☐
		First Day Cover (Ordinary)		12·00	☐	
		First Day Cover (Phosphor)		12·00	☐	

31 Flight of Spitfires   232 Pilot in Hurricane

33 Wing-tips of Spitfire and   234 Spitfires attacking Heinkel
Messerschmitt 'ME-109'   'HE-111' Bomber

35 Spitfire attacking Stuka   236 Hurricanes over Wreck of
Dive-bomber   Dornier 'DO-17z2' Bomber

The above were issued together se-tenant in blocks of six (3 × 2) within
the sheet.

37 Anti-aircraft Artillery   238 Air-battle over St Paul's
in Action   Cathedral

25th Anniversary of Battle of Britain
1965 (13 SEPT.)

671	231	4d olive and black	30	35	☐	☐
	a.	Block of 6				
		Nos. 671/6	5·00	5·00	☐	☐
	p.	Phosphor	40	50	☐	☐
	pa.	Block of 6				
		Nos. 671p/6p	10·50	8·00	☐	☐
672	232	4d olive, blackish olive and black	30	35	☐	☐
		p. Phosphor	40	50	☐	☐
673	233	4d multicoloured	30	35	☐	☐
		p. Phosphor	40	50	☐	☐
674	234	4d olive and black	30	35	☐	☐
		p. Phosphor	40	50	☐	☐
675	235	4d olive and black	30	35	☐	☐
		p. Phosphor	40	50	☐	☐
676	236	4d multicoloured	30	35	☐	☐
		p. Phosphor	40	50	☐	☐
677	237	9d violet, orange and purple	1·25	1·25	☐	☐
		p. Phosphor	1·25	80	☐	☐
678	238	1s 3d multicoloured	1·25	1·25	☐	☐
		p. Phosphor	1·25	80	☐	☐
		Set of 8 (Ordinary)	6·50	4·25	☐	☐
		Set of 8 (Phosphor)	12·00	4·25	☐	☐
		First Day Cover (Ordinary)		18·00	☐	
		First Day Cover (Phosphor)		18·00	☐	
		Presentation Pack (Ordinary)	48·00		☐	

239 Tower and Georgian   240 Tower and 'Nash' Terrace,
Buildings   Regent's Park

Opening of Post Office Tower
1965 (8 OCT.)

679	239	3d yellow, blue and green	10	10	☐	☐
		p. Phosphor	10	10	☐	☐
680	240	1s 3d green and blue	65	75	☐	☐
		p. Phosphor	50	50	☐	☐
		Set of 2 (Ordinary)	75	85	☐	☐
		Set of 2 (Phosphor)	60	60	☐	☐
		First Day Cover (Ordinary)		7·00	☐	
		First Day Cover (Phosphor)		8·00	☐	
		Presentation Pack (Ordinary)	2·50		☐	
		Presentation Pack (Phosphor)	2·50		☐	

241 U.N. Emblem   242 I.C.Y. Emblem

20th Anniversary of UNO and International Co-operation Year

1965 (25 Oct.)

681	**241**	3d blk, orge & bl ..	15	20	☐	☐
		p. Phosphor ..	25	25	☐	☐
682	**242**	1s 6d blk, pur & bl ..	1·10	90	☐	☐
		p. Phosphor ..	2·50	2·50	☐	☐
		Set of 2 (Ordinary) ..	1·25	1·10	☐	☐
		Set of 2 (Phosphor) ..	2·75	2·75	☐	☐
		First Day Cover (Ordinary) ..		9·00		☐
		First Day Cover (Phosphor)		10·00		☐

243 Telecommunications Network   244 Radio Waves and Switchboard

I.T.U. Centenary

1965 (15 Nov.)

683	**243**	9d multicoloured ..	20	20	☐	☐
		p. Phosphor ..	60	50	☐	☐
684	**244**	1s 6d multicoloured ..	1·40	1·10	☐	☐
		p. Phosphor ..	6·00	6·00	☐	☐
		Set of 2 (Ordinary) ..	1·50	1·25	☐	☐
		Set of 2 (Phosphor) ..	6·50	6·50	☐	☐
		First Day Cover (Ordinary) ..		11·00		☐
		First Day Cover (Phosphor)		11·00		☐

245 Robert Burns (after Skirving chalk drawing)   246 Robert Burns (after Nasmyth portrait)

Burns Commemoration

1966 (25 Jan.)

685	**245**	4d blk, indigo & bl ..	15	15	☐	☐
		p. Phosphor	25	25	☐	☐
686	**246**	1s 3d blk, bl & orge ..	70	70	☐	☐
		p. Phosphor	1·00	1·00	☐	☐
		Set of 2 (Ordinary) ..	85	85	☐	☐
		Set of 2 (Phosphor) ..	1·25	1·25	☐	☐
		First Day Cover (Ordinary) ..		3·00		☐
		First Day Cover (Phosphor)		3·50		☐
		Presentation Pack (Ordinary)	30·00			☐

247 Westminster Abbey   248 Fan Vaulting, Henry VII Chapel

900th Anniversary of Westminster Abbey

1966 (28 Feb.)   *Perf* 15×14 (3d) or 11×12 (2s 6d)

687	**247**	3d black, brown and blue ..	15	10	☐	☐
		p. Phosphor ..	30	30	☐	☐
688	**248**	2s 6d black	85	90	☐	☐
		Set of 2	1·00	1·00	☐	☐
		First Day Cover (Ordinary) ..		6·50		☐
		First Day Cover (Phosphor)		7·50		☐
		Presentation Pack (Ordinary)	16·00			☐

249 View near Hassocks, Sussex   250 Antrim, Northern Ireland

251 Harlech Castle, Wales   252 Cairngorm Mountains, Scotland

Landscapes

1966 (2 May)

689	**249**	4d black, yellow-green and blue	15	15	☐	☐
		p. Phosphor ..	15	15	☐	☐
690	**250**	6d black, green and blue ..	15	15	☐	☐
		p. Phosphor ..	25	25	☐	☐
691	**251**	1s 3d black, yellow and blue ..	35	35	☐	☐
		p. Phosphor ..	35	35	☐	☐
692	**252**	1s 6d black, orange and blue ..	50	50	☐	☐
		p. Phosphor ..	50	50	☐	☐
		Set of 4 (Ordinary) ..	1·00	1·00	☐	☐
		Set of 4 (Phosphor) ..	1·00	1·00	☐	☐
		First Day Cover (Ordinary)		7·00		☐
		First Day Cover (Phosphor)		7·00		☐

4d

4d ENGLAND WINNERS

World Cup 1966 / HARRISON AND SONS LTD

253 Players with Ball

260 Cup Winners

WILLIAM KEMPSTER / HARRISON AND SONS LTD / 6d

WORLD CUP 1966 / 1/3 / DAVID CAPLAN / HARRISON AND SONS LTD

254 Goalmouth Mêlée

255 Goalkeeper saving Goal

World Cup Football Competition

1966 (1 June)

693	**253**	4d	multicoloured ..	15	10	□	□
		p.	Phosphor ..	15	10	□	□
694	**254**	6d	multicoloured ..	20	20	□	□
		p.	Phosphor ..	20	20	□	□
695	**255**	1s 3d	multicoloured ..	50	50	□	□
		p.	Phosphor ..	50	50	□	□
		Set of 3 (Ordinary) ..		75	75	□	□
		Set of 3 (Phosphor) ..		75	75	□	□
		First Day Cover (Ordinary) ..			7·00		□
		First Day Cover (Phosphor)			7·00		□
		Presentation Pack (Ordinary)		13·00		□	

BLACK-HEADED GULL / J NORRIS WOOD / 4d / HARRISON AND SONS LTD

BLUE TIT / J NORRIS WOOD / 4d / HARRISON AND SONS LTD

256 Black-headed Gull

257 Blue Tit

ROBIN / J NORRIS WOOD / 4d / HARRISON AND SONS LTD

BLACKBIRD / J NORRIS WOOD / 4d / HARRISON AND SONS LTD

258 Robin

259 Blackbird

The above were issued *se-tenant* in blocks of four within the sheet.

British Birds

1966 (8 Aug.)

696	**256**	4d	multicoloured ..	10	15	□	□
		a.	*Block of 4*				
			Nos. 696/9 ..	1·00	1·00	□	□
		p.	Phosphor ..	10	15	□	□
		pa.	*Block of 4*				
			Nos. 696p/9p ..	1·00	1·00	□	□
697	**257**	4d	multicoloured ..	10	15	□	□
		p.	Phosphor ..	10	15	□	□
698	**258**	4d	multicoloured ..	10	15	□	□
		p.	Phosphor ..	10	15	□	□
699	**259**	4d	multicoloured ..	10	15	□	□
		p.	Phosphor ..	10	15	□	□
		Set of 4 (Ordinary)		1·00	50	□	□
		Set of 4 (Phosphor)		1·00	50	□	□
		First Day Cover (Ordinary) ..			7·00		□
		First Day Cover (Phosphor)			7·00		□
		Presentation Pack (Ordinary)		7·00		□	

England's World Cup Football Victory

1966 (18 Aug.)

700	**260**	4d	multicoloured ..	20	20	□	□
		First Day Cover			2·00		□

4d / D GILLESPIE / HARRISON AND SONS LTD

6d / D GILLESPIE / HARRISON AND SONS LTD

261 Jodrell Bank Radio Telescope

262 British Motor-cars

SR N6 Hovercraft / 1/3 / J ANDREW RESTALL / HARRISON AND SONS LTD

Nuclear power / J ANDREW RESTALL / 1/6 / HARRISON AND SONS LTD

263 SR N6 Hovercraft

264 Windscale Reactor

British Technology

1966 (19 Sept.)

701	**261**	4d	black and lemon	15	15	□	□
		p.	Phosphor ..	15	15	□	□
702	**262**	6d	red, blue and orange ..	15	15	□	□
		p.	Phosphor ..	15	15	□	□
703	**263**	1s 3d	multicoloured ..	30	40	□	□
		p.	Phosphor ..	45	50	□	□
704	**264**	1s 6d	multicoloured ..	50	45	□	□
		p.	Phosphor ..	65	60	□	□
		Set of 4 (Ordinary)		1·00	1·00	□	□
		Set of 4 (Phosphor)		1·25	1·25	□	□
		First Day Cover (Ordinary) ..			3·00		□
		First Day Cover (Phosphor)			3·00		□
		Presentation Pack (Ordinary)		7·00		□	

265

266

267

268

269

270

The above show battle scenes, they were issued together *se-tenant* in horizontal strips of six within the sheet.

271 Norman Ship

272 Norman Horsemen attacking Harold's Troops

900th Anniversary of Battle of Hastings

1966 (14 OCT.) *Designs show scenes from Bayeux Tapestry.*
Wmk 179 (*sideways on 1s 3d*)

705	**265**	4d multicoloured ..	10	15	☐	☐
	a.	*Strip of 6*				
		Nos. 705/10 ..	2·00	2·00	☐	☐
	p.	*Phosphor* ..	10	25	☐	☐
	pa.	*Strip of 6*				
		Nos. 705p/10p	2·00	2·00	☐	☐
706	**266**	4d multicoloured ..	10	15	☐	☐
	p.	*Phosphor* ..	10	25	☐	☐
707	**267**	4d multicoloured ..	10	15	☐	☐
	p.	*Phosphor* ..	10	25	☐	☐
708	**268**	4d multicoloured ..	10	15	☐	☐
	p.	*Phosphor* ..	10	25	☐	☐
709	**269**	4d multicoloured ..	10	15	☐	☐
	p.	*Phosphor* ..	10	25	☐	☐
710	**270**	4d multicoloured ..	10	15	☐	☐
	p.	*Phosphor* ..	10	25	☐	☐
711	**271**	6d multicoloured ..	10	10	☐	☐
	p.	*Phosphor* ..	10	10	☐	☐
712	**272**	1s 3d multicoloured ..	20	20	☐	☐
	p.	*Phosphor* ..	20	20	☐	☐
		Set of 8 (Ordinary)	2·00	1·10	☐	
		Set of 8 (Phosphor)	2·00	1·60	☐	
		First Day Cover (Ordinary)		3·00		☐
		First Day Cover (Phosphor)		3·00		☐
		Presentation Pack (Ordinary)	7·00		☐	

273 King of the Orient

274 Snowman

Christmas

1966 (1 DEC.) **Wmk 179** (*upright on 1s 6d*)

713	**273**	3d multicoloured ..	10	10	☐	☐
	p.	*Phosphor* ..	10	10	☐	☐
714	**274**	1s 6d multicoloured ..	35	35	☐	☐
	p.	*Phosphor* ..	35	35	☐	☐
		Set of 2 (Ordinary)	45	45	☐	☐
		Set of 2 (Phosphor)	45	45	☐	☐
		First Day Cover (Ordinary)		1·50		☐
		First Day Cover (Phosphor)		1·50		☐
		Presentation Pack (Ordinary)	7·00		☐	

275 Sea Freight

276 Air Freight

European Free Trade Association (EFTA)

1967 (20 FEB.)

715	**275**	9d multicoloured ..	15	15	☐	☐
	p.	*Phosphor* ..	15	15	☐	☐
716	**276**	1s 6d multicoloured ..	30	30	☐	☐
	p.	*Phosphor* ..	30	30	☐	☐
		Set of 2 (Ordinary)	40	40	☐	☐
		Set of 2 (Phosphor)	40	40	☐	☐
		First Day Cover (Ordinary)		1·50		☐
		First Day Cover (Phosphor)		1·50		☐
		Presentation Pack (Ordinary)	1·50		☐	

277 Hawthorn and Bramble

278 Larger Bindweed and Viper's Bugloss

279 Ox-eye Daisy, Coltsfoot and Buttercup

280 Bluebell, Red Campion and Wood Anemone

The above were issued together *se-tenant* in blocks of four within the sheet.

281 Dog Violet

282 Primroses

British Wild Flowers

1967 (24 APR.)

717	277	4d multicoloured ..	15	10	□	□
		a. Block of 4				
		Nos. 717/20 ..	1·25	1·25	□	□
		p. Phosphor ..	10	10	□	□
		pa. Block of 4				
		Nos. 717p/20p	1·00	1·00	□	□
718	278	4d multicoloured ..	15	10	□	□
		p. Phosphor ..	10	10	□	□
719	279	4d multicoloured ..	15	10	□	□
		p. Phosphor ..	10	10	□	□
720	280	4d multicoloured ..	15	10	□	□
		p. Phosphor ..	10	10	□	□
721	281	9d multicoloured ..	15	10	□	□
		p. Phosphor ..	10	10	□	□
722	282	1s 9d multicoloured ..	20	20	□	□
		p. Phosphor ..	30	20	□	□
		Set of 6 (Ordinary)	1·40	65	□	□
		Set of 6 (Phosphor)	1·25	65	□	□
		First Day Cover (Ordinary)		2·50		□
		First Day Cover (Phosphor)		2·50		□
		Presentation Pack (Ordinary)	3·00			□
		Presentation Pack (Phosphor)	3·00			□

PRESENTATION PACKS IN FOREIGN LANGUAGES

German Presentation Packs are similar to the English versions but have the text printed in German. From the 1969 Collectors Pack until the end of 1974 they were replaced by separately printed insert cards in German. Similar cards in Japanese and Dutch were available from 1969 British Ships issue until end of 1974. A pack printed in Japanese was, however, issued for the 1972 Royal Silver Wedding set.

283 (value at left)

284 (value at right)

I   II

Two types of the 2d.
I. Value spaced away from left side of stamp.
II. Value close to left side from new multi-positive. This results in the portrait appearing in the centre, thus conforming with the other values.

1967–69 *Two phosphor bands, except where otherwise stated. No wmk*

723	283	½d orange-brown	10	20	□	□
724		1d olive (2 bands)	10	10	□	□
725		1d olive (1 centre band)	25	30	□	□
726		2d lake-brown (Type I) (2 bands)	10	15	□	□
727		2d lake-brown (Type II) (2 bands)	15	15	□	□
728		2d lake-brown (Type II) (1 centre band) ..	40	50	□	□
729		3d violet (1 centre band)	10	10	□	□
730		3d violet (2 bands)	30	30	□	□
731		4d sepia (2 bands)	10	10	□	□
732		4d olive-brown (1 centre band) ..	10	10	□	□
733		4d vermilion (1 centre band) ..	10	10	□	□
734		4d vermilion (1 side band) ..	1·40	1·60	□	□
735		5d blue	10	10	□	□
736		6d purple	20	20	□	□
737	284	7d emerald	40	30	□	□
738		8d vermilion ..	15	30	□	□
739		8d turquoise-blue ..	45	50	□	□
740		9d green	50	30	□	□
741	283	10d drab	45	50	□	□
742		1s violet	40	30	□	□
743		1s 6d blue & dp blue ..	50	30	□	□
		c. Phosphorised paper	75	90	□	□
744		1s 9d orange & black	40	30	□	□
		Set of 16 (one of each value and colour)	3·00	3·25	□	□
		Presentation Pack (one of each value)	6·00			□
		Presentation Pack (German)	40·00			□

No 734 exists with the phosphor band at the left or right.
For prices of First Day Covers and for listing of decimal issue, Nos. X841/X1026, see pages 32/6.

285 'Master Lambton'
(Sir Thomas Lawrence)

286 'Mares and Foals in a
Landscape' (George Stubbs)

287 'Children Coming Out
of School' (L. S. Lowry)

288 Gipsy Moth IV

British Paintings

1967 (10 JULY) *Two phosphor bands. No wmk*

748	**285**	4d multicoloured	..	10		10	☐	☐
749	**286**	9d multicoloured	..	20		20	☐	☐
750	**287**	1s 6d multicoloured	..	35		25	☐	☐
		Set of 3	.. .. ..	50		50	☐	☐
		First Day Cover ..	.. ..		1·50			☐
		Presentation Pack	.. ..	5·50				☐

Sir Francis Chichester's World Voyage

1967 (24 JULY) *Three phosphor bands. No wmk*

751	**288**	1s 9d multicoloured	..	25		25	☐	☐
		First Day Cover	.. .. ..		1·00			☐

289 Radar Screen

290 *Penicillium notatum*

291 'VC-10' Jet Engines

292 Television Equipment

British Discovery and Invention

1967 (19 SEPT.) *Two phosphor bands (except 4d, three
bands). Wmk **179** (sideways on 1s 9d)*

752	**289**	4d yell, blk & verm..	10		10	☐	☐
753	**290**	1s multicoloured	10		10	☐	☐
754	**291**	1s 6d multicoloured ..	25		15	☐	☐
755	**292**	1s 9d multicoloured ..	30		20	☐	☐
		Set of 4	60		50	☐	☐
		First Day Cover		1·00			☐
		Presentation Pack	2·00				☐

NO WATERMARK. All the following issues are on un
watermarked paper unless stated.

293 'The Adoration of
the Shepherds'
(School of Seville)

294 'Madonna and
Child' (Murillo)

295 'The Adoration of the Shepherd
(Louis Le Nain)

Christmas

1967 *Two phosphor bands (except 3d, one phosphor band*

756	**293**	3d multicoloured (27 Nov.) ..	10		10	☐	☐
757	**294**	4d multicoloured (18 Oct.) ..	10		10	☐	☐
758	**295**	1s 6d multicoloured (27 Nov.)	35		35	☐	☐
		Set of 3	50		50	☐	☐
		First Day Covers (2)		1·00			☐

Gift Pack 1967

1967 (27 Nov.) *Comprises Nos. 715p/22p and 748/58*

	Gift Pack	2·75		☐

1967–68 *No wmk* *Perf 11×12*

759	**166**	2s 6d brown	.. ..	40	50	☐	☐
760	**167**	5s red ..	.. ..	1·00	1·00	☐	☐
761	**168**	10s blue	.. ..	5·00	5·50	☐	☐
762	**169**	£1 black	.. ..	4·00	4·00	☐	☐
		Set of 4	.. ..	9·00	10·00	☐	☐

296 Tarr Steps, Exmoor

297 Aberfeldy Bridge

298 Menai Bridge

299 M4 Viaduct

British Bridges

1968 (29 APR.) *Two phosphor bands*

763	296	4d multicoloured ..	10	10	☐	☐
764	297	9d multicoloured ..	10	10	☐	☐
765	298	1s 6d multicoloured ..	20	15	☐	☐
766	299	1s 9d multicoloured ..	25	30	☐	☐
		Set of 4	60	60	☐	☐
		First Day Cover		1·10	☐	
		Presentation Pack	2·00		☐	

300 'TUC' and Trades Unionists

301 Mrs Emmeline Pankhurst (statue)

302 Sopwith 'Camel' and 'Lightning' Fighters

303 Captain Cook's *Endeavour* and Signature

British Anniversaries. Events described on stamps

1968 (29 MAY) *Two phosphor bands*

767	300	4d multicoloured ..	10	10	☐	☐
768	301	9d violet, grey and black	10	10	☐	☐
769	302	1s multicoloured ..	20	20	☐	☐
770	303	1s 9d ochre and brown	25	25	☐	☐
		Set of 4	60	60	☐	☐
		First Day Cover		3·25	☐	
		Presentation Pack	3·00		☐	

304 'Queen Elizabeth I' (Unknown Artist)

305 'Pinkie' (Lawrence)

306 'Ruins of St Mary Le Port' (Piper)

307 'The Hay Wain' (Constable)

British Paintings

1968 (12 AUG.) *Two phosphor bands*

771	304	4d multicoloured ..	10	10	☐	☐
772	305	1s multicoloured ..	15	15	☐	☐
773	306	1s 6d multicoloured ..	20	20	☐	☐
774	307	1s 9d multicoloured ..	25	25	☐	☐
		Set of 4	60	60	☐	☐
		First Day Cover		1·00	☐	
		Presentation Pack	2·00		☐	
		Presentation Pack (German)	6·00		☐	

Gift Pack 1968

1968 (16 SEPT.) *Comprises Nos. 763/74*

Gift Pack	6·00		☐
Gift Pack (German)	21·00		☐

Collectors Pack 1968

1968 (16 SEPT.) *Comprises Nos. 752/8 and 763/74*

Collectors Pack	6·00		☐

308 Girl and Boy with Rocking Horse

309 Girl with Doll's House

310 Boy with Train Set

Christmas

1968 (25 Nov.) *Two phosphor bands (except 4d, one centre phosphor band)*

775	**308**	4d multicoloured ..	10	10	☐	☐
776	**309**	9d multicoloured ..	15	15	☐	☐
777	**310**	1s 6d multicoloured ..	25	25	☐	☐
		Set of 3	50	50	☐	☐
		First Day Cover		1·00		☐
		Presentation Pack ..	2·00		☐	
		Presentation Pack (German)	6·00		☐	

311 RMS *Queen Elizabeth 2*

312 Elizabethan Galleon

313 East Indiaman

314 Cutty Sark

315 SS *Great Britain*

The 9d and 1s values were arranged in horizontal strips of three and pairs respectively throughout the sheet.

RMS Mauretania

316 RMS *Mauretan*

British Ships

1969 (15 Jan.) *Two phosphor bands (except 5d, one hor. phosphor band, 1s, two vert phosphor bands at right)*

778	**311**	5d multicoloured ..	10	10	☐	☐
779	**312**	9d multicoloured ..	10	15	☐	☐
		a. Strip of 3				
		Nos. 779/81 ..	85	85	☐	☐
780	**313**	9d multicoloured ..	10	15	☐	☐
781	**314**	9d multicoloured ..	10	15	☐	☐
782	**315**	1s multicoloured ..	25	25	☐	☐
		a. Pair. Nos. 782/3	90	85	☐	☐
783	**316**	1s multicoloured ..	25	25	☐	☐
		Set of 6	1·60	90	☐	☐
		First Day Cover		3·25		☐
		Presentation Pack ..	3·00		☐	
		Presentation Pack (German)	22·00		☐	

317 'Concorde' in Flight

318 Plan and Elevation Views

319 'Concorde's' Nose and Tail

320 (See also Type 359a)

First Flight of 'Concorde'

1969 (3 Mar.) *Two phosphor bands*

784	**317**	4d multicoloured ..	10	10	☐	☐
785	**318**	9d multicoloured ..	20	20	☐	☐
786	**319**	1s 6d deep blue, grey				
		and light blue ..	30	30	☐	☐
		Set of 3	50	50	☐	☐
		First Day Cover		1·25		☐
		Presentation Pack ..	2·50		☐	
		Presentation Pack (German)	18·00		☐	

1969 (5 Mar.) *P* 12

787	**320**	2s 6d brown	50	30	☐	☐
788		5s lake	2·25	60	☐	☐
789		10s ultramarine ..	7·00	7·50	☐	☐
790		£1 black	3·00	1·60	☐	☐
		Set of 4	11·50	9·00	☐	☐
		Presentation Pack ..	18·00		☐	
		Presentation Pack (German)	40·00		☐	

21 Page from the *Daily Mail*, and Vickers 'Vimy' Aircraft

322 Europa and C.E.P.T. Emblems

323 I.L.O. Emblem

324 Flags of N.A.T.O. Countries

325 Vickers 'Vimy' Aircraft and Globe showing Flight

Anniversaries. Events described on stamps

1969 (2 APR.) *Two phosphor bands*

791	321	5d multicoloured ..	10	10	☐	☐
792	322	9d multicoloured ..	20	20	☐	☐
793	323	1s claret, red and				
		blue	20	20	☐	☐
794	324	1s 6d multicoloured ..	20	20	☐	☐
795	325	1s 9d olive, yellow and				
		turquoise-green	25	25	☐	☐
		Set of 5	85	85	☐	☐
		First Day Cover		1·50		☐
		Presentation Pack	2·50			☐
		Presentation Pack (German)	40·00			☐

326 Durham Cathedral

327 York Minster

328 St Giles' Cathedral, Edinburgh

329 Canterbury Cathedral

The above were issued together *se-tenant* in blocks of four within the sheet.

330 St Paul's Cathedral

331 Liverpool Metropolitan Cathedral

British Architecture (Cathedrals)

1969 (28 MAY) *Two phosphor bands*

796	326	5d multicoloured ..	10	10	☐	☐
	a	Block of 4				
		Nos. 796/9 ..	85	1·00	☐	☐
797	327	5d multicoloured ..	10	10	☐	☐
798	328	5d multicoloured ..	10	10	☐	☐
799	329	5d multicoloured ..	10	10	☐	☐
800	330	9d multicoloured ..	15	15	☐	☐
801	331	1s 6d multicoloured ..	15	15	☐	☐
		Set of 6	1·00	55	☐	☐
		First Day Cover		2·00		☐
		Presentation Pack	3·00			☐
		Presentation Pack (German)	22·00			☐

332 The King's Gate, Caernarvon Castle

333 The Eagle Tower, Caernarvon Castle

334 Queen Eleanor's Gate, Caernarvon Castle

335 Celtic Cross, Margam Abbey

The 5d values were printed *se-tenant* in strips of three throughout the sheet.

336 Prince Charles

337 Mahatma Gandhi

Investiture of H.R.H. The Prince of Wales

1969 (1 July) *Two phosphor bands*

802	**332**	5d multicoloured ..	10	10	☐	☐
		a. Strip of 3				
		Nos. 802/4 ..	70	75	☐	☐
803	**333**	5d multicoloured ..	10	10	☐	☐
804	**334**	5d multicoloured ..	10	10	☐	☐
805	**335**	9d multicoloured ..	20	10	☐	☐
806	**336**	1s black and gold	20	10	☐	☐
		Set of 5	1·00	45	☐	☐
		First Day Cover		1·25		☐
		Presentation Pack	2·00		☐	
		Presentation Pack (German)	16·00		☐	

Gandhi Centenary Year

1969 (13 Aug.) *Two phosphor bands*

807	**337**	1s 6d multicoloured ..	30	30	☐	☐
		First Day Cover		1·00		☐

Collectors Pack 1969

1969 (15 Sept.) *Comprises Nos. 775/86 and 791/807*

	Collectors Pack	22·00	☐

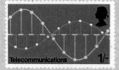

338 National Giro

339 Telecommunications

340 Telecommunications

341 Automatic Sorting

British Post Office Technology

1969 (1 Oct.) *Two phosphor bands* Perf 13½ × 14

808	**338**	5d multicoloured ..	10	10	☐	☐
809	**339**	9d green, bl & blk ..	15	15	☐	☐
810	**340**	1s green, lav & blk..	15	15	☐	☐
811	**341**	1s 6d multicoloured ..	40	40	☐	☐
		Set of 4	70	70	☐	☐
		First Day Cover		1·00		☐
		Presentation Pack	2·25		☐	

342 Herald Angel

343 The Three Shepherds

344 The Three Kings

Christmas

1969 (26 Nov.) *Two phosphor bands (5d, 1s 6d) or one centre band (4d)*

812	**342**	4d multicoloured ..	10	10	☐	☐
813	**343**	5d multicoloured ..	10	10	☐	☐
814	**344**	1s 6d multicoloured ..	30	30	☐	☐
		Set of 3	45	45	☐	☐
		First Day Cover		1·00		☐
		Presentation Pack	2·25		☐	

345 Fife Harling

346 Cotswold Limestone

347 Welsh Stucco

348 Ulster Thatch

British Rural Architecture

1970 (11 Feb.) *Two phosphor bands*

815	**345**	5d multicoloured ..	10	10	☐	☐
816	**346**	9d multicoloured ..	20	20	☐	☐
817	**347**	1s multicoloured ..	20	20	☐	☐
818	**348**	1s 6d multicoloured ..	35	35	☐	☐
		Set of 4	75	75	☐	☐
		First Day Cover		1·25		☐
		Presentation Pack	3·00		☐	

349 Signing the Declaration of Arbroath

350 Florence Nightingale attending Patients

351 Signing of International Co-operative Alliance

352 Pilgrims and *Mayflower*

353 Sir William Herschel, Francis Baily, Sir John Herschel and Telescope

Anniversaries. Events described on stamps

1970 (1 APR.) *Two phosphor bands*

819	**349**	5d multicoloured ..	10	10	☐	☐
820	**350**	9d multicoloured ..	15	15	☐	☐
821	**351**	1s multicoloured ..	25	15	☐	☐
822	**352**	1s 6d multicoloured ..	30	30	☐	☐
823	**353**	1s 9d multicoloured ..	30	30	☐	☐
		Set of 5	1·00	90	☐	☐
		First Day Cover		1·50		☐
		Presentation Pack	3·00			☐

354 'Mr Pickwick and Sam' (*Pickwick Papers*)

355 'Mr and Mrs Micawber' (*David Copperfield*)

356 'David Copperfield and Betsy Trotwood' (*David Copperfield*)

357 'Oliver asking for more' (*Oliver Twist*)

The 5d values were issued together *se-tenant* in blocks of four within the sheet.

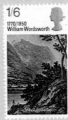

358 'Grasmere' (from engraving by J. Farrington, R.A.)

Literary Anniversaries. Events described on stamps

1970 (3 JUNE) *Two phosphor bands*

824	**354**	5d multicoloured ..	10	10	☐	☐
		a. Block of 4				
		Nos. 824/7 ..	90	90	☐	☐
825	**355**	5d multicoloured ..	10	10	☐	☐
826	**356**	5d multicoloured ..	10	10	☐	☐
827	**357**	5d multicoloured ..	10	10	☐	☐
828	**358**	1s 6d multicoloured ..	20	20	☐	☐
		Set of 5	1·00	55	☐	☐
		First Day Cover		2·00		☐
		Presentation Pack	3·00			☐

359

359a (Value redrawn)

Decimal Currency

1970 (17 JUNE)–**72** *10p and some printings of the 50p were issued on phosphor paper* *Perf* 12

829	**359**	10p cerise	1·00	75	☐	☐
830		20p olive-green ..	70	15	☐	☐
831		50p ultramarine ..	1·50	40	☐	☐
831b	**359a**	£1 black	3·50	75	☐	☐
		Set of 4	6·00	1·75	☐	☐
829/31		*Presentation Pack* ..	7·00			☐
790 (*or* 831b), 830/1						
		Presentation Pack ..	8·00			☐

For First Day Cover prices see page 36.

360 Runners

361 Swimmers

362 Cyclists

Ninth British Commonwealth Games

1970 (15 July) *Two phosphor bands*   *Perf* 13½ × 14

832	360	5d	pink, emerald, greenish yellow & yellow-green	10	10	☐	☐
833	361	1s 6d	greenish blue, lilac, brown and Prussian blue ..	50	50	☐	☐
834	362	1s 9d	yellow-orange, lilac, salmon and red-brown ..	50	50	☐	☐
		Set of 3		1·00	1·00	☐	☐
		First Day Cover			1·25		☐
		Presentation Pack		2·50		☐	

Collectors Pack 1970

1970 (14 Sept.) *Comprises Nos. 808/28 and 832/4*

	Collectors Pack	.. .. ..	26·00		☐

5d
Philympia 1970

9d
Philympia 1970

1/6
Philympia 1970

1840 first engraved issue

1847 first embossed issue

1855 first surface printed issue

363 1d Black (1840)

364 1s Green (1847)

365 4d Carmine (1855)

'Philympia 70' Stamp Exhibition

1970 (18 Sept.) *Two phosphor bands*   *Perf* 14 × 14½

835	363	5d	multicoloured ..	10	10	☐	☐
836	364	9d	multicoloured ..	35	35	☐	☐
837	365	1s 6d	multicoloured ..	40	40	☐	☐
		Set of 3		75	75	☐	☐
		First Day Cover			1·25		☐
		Presentation Pack		2·50		☐	

4d

366 Shepherds and Apparition of the Angel

5d

367 Mary, Joseph, and Christ in the Manger

1/6

368 The Wise Men bearing Gifts

Christmas

1970 (25 Nov.) *Two phosphor bands* (5d, 1s 6d) *or one centre phosphor band* (4d)

838	366	4d	multicoloured ..	10	10	☐	☐
839	367	5d	multicoloured ..	10	10	☐	☐
840	368	1s 6d	multicoloured ..	35	35	☐	☐
		Set of 3		50	50	☐	☐
		First Day Cover			1·00		☐
		Presentation Pack		2·50		☐	

75p

369

75p

369a

Decimal Currency
1971–92. Type 369

(a) *Printed in photogravure by Harrison and Sons with phosphor bands. Perf* 15 × 14

X841	½p	turq-bl (2 bands) ..	10	10	☐	☐
X842	½p	turq-bl (1 side band) ..	60·00	25·00	☐	☐
X843	½p	turquoise-blue (1 centre band) ..	30	20	☐	☐
X844	1p	crimson (2 bands) ..	10	10	☐	☐
X845	1p	crim (1 centre band) ..	20	20	☐	☐
X846	1p	crimson ('all-over' phosphor)	20	20	☐	☐
X847	1p	crimson (1 side band)	1·00	1·00	☐	☐
X848	1½p	black (2 bands) ..	20	15	☐	☐
X849	2p	myr-grn (face value as in T **369**) (2 bands) ..	20	10	☐	☐
X850	2p	myr-grn (face value as in T **369**) 'all-over' phosphor	20	15	☐	☐
X851	2½p	mag (1 centre band) ..	15	10	☐	☐
X852	2½p	magenta (1 side band)	1·75	1·75	☐	☐
X853	2½p	magenta (2 bands) ..	30	50	☐	☐
X854	2½p	rose-red (2 bands) ..	50	60	☐	☐
X855	3p	ultramarine (2 bands) ..	20	10	☐	☐
X856	3p	ultram (1 centre band)	20	25	☐	☐
X857	3p	bright magenta (2 bands) ..	30	25	☐	☐
X858	3½p	olive-grey (2 bands) ..	30	30	☐	☐
X859	3½p	ol-grey (1 centre band)	30	15	☐	☐

X860	3½p purple-brown (1 centre band) ..	1·50	1·25	□ □
X861	4p ochre-brown (2 bands)	20	20	□ □
X862	4p greenish bl (2 bands)	2·00	1·75	□ □
X863	4p greenish blue (1 centre band) ..	1·00	1·00	□ □
X864	4p greenish blue (1 side band) ..	1·50	1·50	□ □
X865	4½p grey-blue (2 bands) ..	20	25	□ □
X866	5p pale violet (2 bands)	20	10	□ □
X867	5p claret (1 centre band)	1·50	1·50	□ □
X868	5½p violet (2 bands) ..	25	25	□ □
X869	5½p violet (1 centre band)	20	20	□ □
X870	6p light emerald (2 bands)	30	15	□ □
X871	6½p greenish bl (2 bands)	45	45	□ □
X872	6½p greenish blue (1 centre band) ..	30	15	□ □
X873	6½p greenish blue (1 side band) ..	60	55	□ □
X874	7p purple-brn (2 bands)	35	25	□ □
X875	7p purple-brown (1 centre band) ..	35	20	□ □
X876	7p purple-brown (1 side band) ..	60	75	□ □
X877	7½p chestnut (2 bands) ..	30	25	□ □
X878	8p rosine (2 bands) ..	25	20	□ □
X879	8p rosine (1 centre band)	25	15	□ □
X880	8p rosine (1 side band) ..	60	60	□ □
X881	8½p yellowish green (2 bands) ..	35	20	□ □
X882	9p yellow-orange and black (2 bands) ..	60	30	□ □
X883	9p deep violet (2 bands)	45	25	□ □
X884	9½p purple (2 bands)	45	30	□ □
X885	10p orange-brown and chestnut (2 bands)	40	30	□ □
X886	10p orange-brn (2 bands)	40	20	□ □
X887	10p orange-brown ('all-over' phosphor) ..	30	45	□ □
X888	10p orange-brown (1 centre band) ..	30	20	□ □
X889	10p orange-brown (1 side band) ..	60	60	□ □
X890	10½p yellow (2 bands) ..	40	30	□ □
X891	10½p blue (2 bands) ..	60	45	□ □
X892	11p brown-red (2 bands)	60	25	□ □
X893	11½p drab (1 centre band) ..	45	30	□ □
X894	11½p drab (1 side band)	60	60	□ □
X895	12p yellowish green (2 bands)	60	40	□ □
X896	12p bright emerald (1 centre band) ..	60	40	□ □
X897	12p bright emerald (1 side band) ..	75	75	□ □
X898	12½p light emerald (1 centre band) ..	45	25	□ □
X899	12½p light emerald (1 side band) ..	60	60	□ □
X900	13p pale chestnut (1 centre band) ..	50	35	□ □
X901	13p pale chestnut (1 side band) ..	60	60	□ □
X902	14p grey-blue (2 bands) ..	50	45	□ □
X903	14p dp bl (1 centre band)	60	40	□ □
X904	14p dp blue (1 side band)	1·75	1·75	□ □
X905	15p brt bl (1 centre band)	25	20	□ □
X906	15p brt blue (1 side band)	1·75	1·75	□ □
X907	15½p pale violet (2 bands) ..	45	45	□ □
X908	16p olive-drab (2 bands)	1·25	1·75	□ □
X909	17p grey-blue (2 bands)	75	75	□ □
X910	17p dp bl (1 centre band)	50	50	□ □
X911	17p dp bl (1 side band)	75	75	□ □
X912	18p dp ol-grey (2 bands)	75	75	□ □
X913	18p bright green (1 centre band) ..	30	35	□ □
X914	19p bright orange-red (2 bands) ..	1·00	1·00	□ □
X915	20p dull purple (2 bands)	75	40	□ □
X916	20p brownish black (2 bands) ..	1·00	1·00	□ □
X917	22p bright orange-red (2 bands) ..	1·00	1·00	□ □
X918	26p rosine (2 bands) ..	5·50	5·50	□ □
X919	31p purple (2 bands) ..	5·50	5·50	□ □
X920	34p ochre-brown (2 bands)	5·50	5·50	□ □
X921	50p ochre-brown (2 bands)	1·75	40	□ □
X922	50p ochre (2 bands) ..	4·50	4·50	□ □

(b) Printed in photogravure by Harrison and Sons on phosphorised paper. Perf 15 × 14

X924	½p turquoise-blue ..	10	10	□ □
X925	1p crimson	10	10	□ □
X926	2p myrtle-green (face value as in T **369**)	10	10	□ □
X927	2p deep green (smaller value as in T **369***a*)	10	10	□ □
X928	2p myr-grn (smaller value as in T **369***a*)	1·00	75	□ □
X929	2½p rose-red ..	20	20	□ □
X930	3p bright magenta ..	20	20	□ □
X931	3½p purple-brown	45	45	□ □
X932	4p greenish blue	25	20	□ □
X933	4p new blue ..	10	10	□ □
X934	5p pale violet ..	30	25	□ □
X935	5p dull red-brown	10	10	□ □
X936	6p olive-yellow	10	15	□ □
X937	7p brownish red ..	2·00	2·00	□ □
X938	8½p yellowish green	30	55	□ □
X939	10p orange-brown	15	20	□ □
X940	10p dull orange	15	15	□ □
X941	11p brown-red	75	75	□ □
X942	11½p ochre-brown	50	45	□ □
X943	12p yellowish green	45	40	□ □
X944	13p olive-grey	60	45	□ □
X945	13½p purple-brown	65	60	□ □
X946	14p grey-blue ..	50	40	□ □
X947	15p ultramarine	50	40	□ □
X948	15½p pale violet	50	40	□ □
X949	16p olive-drab ..	60	30	□ □
X950	16½p pale chestnut	85	75	□ □
X951	17p light emerald	70	40	□ □
X952	17p grey-blue	50	40	□ □
X953	17½p pale chestnut	80	80	□ □
X954	18p deep violet	70	75	□ □
X955	18p deep olive-grey	70	60	□ □
X956	19p bright orange-red ..	60	40	□ □

X957	19½p olive-grey	2·00	1·50	☐	☐
X958	20p dull purple	80	20	☐	☐
X959	20p turquoise-green ..	30	35	☐	☐
X960	20p brownish black	30	30	☐	☐
X961	20½p ultramarine	1·10	85	☐	☐
X962	22p blue	80	45	☐	☐
X963	22p yellow-green ..	60	55	☐	☐
X964	22p bright orange-red ..	35	35	☐	☐
X965	23p brown-red	1·10	60	☐	☐
X966	23p bright green ..	70	40	☐	☐
X967	24p violet	1·40	85	☐	☐
X968	24p Indian red	50	50	☐	☐
X969	24p chestnut	40	45	☐	☐
X970	25p purple	90	90	☐	☐
X971	26p rosine	90	30	☐	☐
X972	26p drab	50	50	☐	☐
X973	27p chestnut	1·00	85	☐	☐
X974	27p violet	55	55	☐	☐
X975	28p deep violet	75	60	☐	☐
X976	28p ochre	65	65	☐	☐
X977	28p deep bluish grey ..	45	50	☐	☐
X978	29p ochre-brown	2·50	1·25	☐	☐
X979	29p deep mauve	1·00	60	☐	☐
X980	30p deep olive-grey	45	50	☐	☐
X981	31p purple	1·25	1·25	☐	☐
X982	31p ultramarine	65	65	☐	☐
X983	32p greenish blue	50	55	☐	☐
X984	33p light emerald	70	70	☐	☐
X985	34p ochre-brown	1·10	80	☐	☐
X986	34p deep bluish grey ..	1·00	80	☐	☐
X987	34p deep mauve	55	60	☐	☐
X988	35p sepia	1·25	75	☐	☐
X989	35p yellow	55	60	☐	☐
X990	37p rosine	60	65	☐	☐
X991	39p bright mauve	60	65	☐	☐

(c) Printed in photogravure by Harrison and Sons on ordinary paper. Perf 15 × 14

X992	50p ochre-brown	1·50	45	☐	☐
X993	75p grey-black (smaller values as T **369**a) ..	1·10	1·25	☐	☐

(d) Printed in photogravure by Harrison and Sons on ordinary paper or phosphorised paper. Perf 15 × 14

X994	50p ochre	75	45	☐	☐

(e) Printed in lithography by John Waddington. Perf 14.

X996	4p greenish blue (2 bands)	20	25	☐	☐
X997	4p greenish blue (phosphorised paper)	25	20	☐	☐
X998	20p dull purple (2 bands)	1·00	40	☐	☐
X999	20p dull purple (phosphorised paper)	1·25	40	☐	☐

(f) Printed in lithography by Questa. Perf 13½ × 14 (Nos X1000, X1003/4 and X1018) or 15 × 14 (others)

X1000	2p emerald-green (face value as in T **369**) (phosphorised paper)	20	20	☐	☐
	a Perf 15 × 14	30	20	☐	☐

X1001	2p bright grn and dp grn (smaller value as in T **369**a) (phosphorised paper)	35	35	☐	☐
X1002	4p greenish blue (phosphorised paper)	50	50	☐	☐
X1003	5p light violet (phosphorised paper)	40	20	☐	☐
X1004	5p claret (phosphorised paper)	50	20	☐	☐
	a Perf 15 × 14 ..	40	25	☐	☐
X1005	13p pale chest (1 centre band)	70	70	☐	☐
X1006	13p pale chest (1 side band)	60	60	☐	☐
X1007	14p dp bl (1 centre band) ..	1·00	50	☐	☐
X1008	17p deep blue (1 centre band)	60	50	☐	☐
X1009	18p deep olive-grey (phosphorised paper)	60	60	☐	☐
X1010	18p dp ol-grey (2 bands)	4·00	4·00	☐	☐
X1010a	18p bright green (1 centre band)	30	30	☐	☐
X1010b	18p bright green (1 side band)	60	60	☐	☐
X1011	19p bright orange-red (phosphorised paper)	1·25	90	☐	☐
X1012	20p dull purple (phosphorised paper)	1·25	1·25	☐	☐
X1013	22p yell-grn (2 bands) ..	4·00	4·00	☐	☐
X1014	22p bright orange-red (phosphorised paper)	75	75	☐	☐
X1014n	24p chestnut (phosphorised paper)	40	40	☐	☐
X1014o	24p chestnut (2 bands) ..	80	80	☐	☐
X1015	33p light emerald (phosphorised paper)	2·00	2·00	☐	☐
X1016	33p light emer (2 bands)	1·10	1·10	☐	☐
X1017	34p ochre-brn (2 bands)	4·00	4·00	☐	☐
X1017a	39p brt mauve (2 bands)	1·25	1·25	☐	☐
X1018	75p black (face value as .. T **369**) (ordinary paper)	3·50 3·00	3·00 1·50	☐	☐
	a Perf 15 × 14	3·00	3·00	☐	☐
X1019	75p brownish grey and black (smaller value as T **369**a) (ordinary paper)	7·50	5·00	☐	☐

(g) Printed in lithography by Walsall. Perf 14

X1020	14p deep blue (1 side band)	3·00	3·00	☐	☐
X1021	19p bright orange-red (2 bands)	1·00	1·00	☐	☐
X1022	29p deep mauve (2 bands)	4·50	3·00	☐	☐
X1023	29p deep mauve (phosphorised paper)	5·50	4·00	☐	☐
X1024	31p ultramarine (phosphorised paper)	1·25	1·25	☐	☐
X1025	33p light emerald (phosphorised paper)	50	55	☐	☐
X1026	39p bright mauve (phosphorised paper)	60	65	☐	☐

Presentation Pack (*contains* ½p (X841), 1p (X844), 1½p (X848), 2p (X849), 2½p (X851), 3p (X855), 3½p (X858), 4p (X861), 5p (X866), 6p (X870), 7½p (X877), 9p (X882)) .. 4·00 ☐

Presentation Pack ('*Scandinavia 71*') (*contents as above*) .. .. .. 32·00 ☐

Presentation Pack (*contains* ½p (X841), 1p (X844), 1½p (X848), 2p (X849), 2½p (X851), 3p (X855 *or* X856), 3½p (X858 *or* X859), 4p (X861), 4½p (X865), 5p (X866), 5½p (X868 *or* X869), 6p (X870), 6½p (X871 *or* X872), 7p (X874), 7½p (X877), 8p (X878), 9p (X882), 10p (X885)) .. .. .. 4·00 ☐

Presentation Pack (*contains* ½p (X841), 1p (X844), 1½p (X848), 2p (X849), 2½p (X851), 3p (X856), 5p (X866), 6½p (X872), 7p (X874 *or* X875), 7½p (X877), 8p (X878), 8½p (X881), 9p (X883), 9½p (X884) 10p (X886), 10½p (X890), 11p (X892) 20p (X915), 50p (X921)) .. .. 5·00 ☐

Presentation Pack (*contains* 2½p (X929), 3p (X930), 4p (X996), 10½p (X891), 11½p (X893), 11½p (X942), 12p (X943), 13p (X944), 13½p (X945), 14p (X946), 15p (X947), 15½p (X948), 17p (X951), 17½p (X953), 18p (X954), 22p (X962), 25p (X970), 75p (X1018)) 16·00 ☐

Presentation Pack (*Contains* ½p (X924), 1p (X925), 2p (X1000), 3p (X930), 3½p (X931), 4p (X997), 5p (X1004), 10p (X888), 12½p (X898), 16p (X949), 16½p (X950), 17p (X952), 20p (X999), 20½p (X961), 23p (X965), 26p (X971), 28p (X975), 31p (X981), 50p (X992), 75p (X1018)) .. .. .. 22·00 ☐

Presentation Pack (*contains* ½p (X924), 1p (X925), 2p (X1000a), 3p (X930), 4p (X997), 5p (X1004a), 10p (X939), 13p (X900), 16p (X949), 17p (X952), 18p (X955), 20p (X999), 22p (X963), 24p (X967), 26p (X971), 28p (X975), 31p (X981), 34p (X985), 50p (X992), 75p (X1018a)) .. .. 18·00 ☐

Presentation Pack (*contains* 1p (X925), 2p (X1000a), 3p (X930), 4p (X997), 5p (X1004a), 7p (X937), 10p (X939), 12p (X896),

13p (X900), 17p (X952), 18p (X955), 20p (X999), 22p (X963), 24p (X967), 26p (X971), 28p (X975), 31p (X981), 34p (X985), 50p (X992), 75p (X1018a)) .. .. 14·00 ☐

Presentation Pack (*contains* 14p (X903), 19p (X956), 20p (X959), 23p (X966), 27p (X973), 28p (X976), 32p (X983), 35p (X988)) 7·00 ☐

Presentation Pack (*contains* 15p (X905), 20p (X960), 24p (X968), 29p (X979), 30p (X980), 34p (X986), 37p (X990) .. .. .. 5·00 ☐

Presentation Pack · (*contains* 10p (X940), 17p (X910), 22p (X964), 26p (X972), 27p (X974), 31p (X982), 33p (X984) .. .. .. 3·25 ☐

Presentation Pack (*contains* 1p (X925), 2p (X927), 3p (X930), 4p (X933), 5p (X935), 10p (X940), 17p (X910), 20p (X959), 22p (X964), 26p (X972), 27p (X974), 30p (X980), 31p (X982), 32p (X983), 33p (X984), 37p (X990), 50p (X994), 75p (X993)) .. .. 7·00 ☐

Presentation Pack (*contains* 6p (X936), 18p (X913), 24p (X969), 28p (X977), 34p (X987), 35p (X989), 39p (X991)) .. .. .. 3·25 ☐

"X" NUMBERS These are provisional only and may be amended in future editions.

PHOSPHOR BANDS See notes on page 15.
Phosphor bands are applied to the stamps, after the design has been printed, by a separate cylinder. On issues with "all-over" phosphor the "band" covers the entire stamp. Parts of the stamp covered by phosphor bands, or the entire surface for "all-over" phosphor versions, appear matt.
Nos. X847, X852, X864, X873, X876, X880, X889, X894, X897, X899, X901, X906, X911 and X1006 exist with the phosphor band at the left or right of the stamp.

PHOSPHORISED PAPER. First introduced as an experiment for a limited printing of the 1s 6d value (No. 743c) in 1969 this paper has the phosphor, to activate the automatic sorting machinery, added to the paper coating before the stamps were printed. Issues on this paper have a completely shiny surface. Although not adopted after this first trial further experiments on the 8½p in 1976 led to this paper being used for new printings of current values.

QUEEN ELIZABETH II DEFINITIVE FIRST DAY COVERS

The British Post Office did not introduce special First Day of Issue postmarks for definitive issues until the first instalment of the Machin £sd series, issued 5 June 1967, although "First Day" treatment had been provided for some Regional stamps from 8 June 1964 onwards.

1952–1966

PRICES for First Day Covers listed below are for stamps, as indicated, used on illustrated envelopes and postmarked with operational cancellations.

5 Dec. 1952	$1\frac{1}{2}d$, $2\frac{1}{2}d$ (*Nos.* 517, 519) ..	6·00	☐
6 July 1953	5*d*, 8*d*, 1s (*Nos.* 522, 525, 529)	25·00	☐
31 Aug. 1953	$\frac{1}{2}d$, 1*d*, 2*d* (*Nos.* 515/16, 518)	20·00	☐
2 Nov. 1953	4*d*, 1s 3*d*, 1s 6*d* (*Nos.* 521, 530/1)	50·00	☐
18 Jan. 1954	3*d*, 6*d*, 7*d* (*Nos.* 520, 523/4)	30·00	☐
8 Feb. 1954	9*d*, 10*d*, 11*d* (*Nos.* 526/8) ..	60·00	☐
1 Sept. 1955	10s, £1 (*Nos.* 538/9)	£400	☐
23 Sept. 1955	2s 6*d*, 5s (*Nos.* 536/7) ..	£175	☐
19 Nov. 1957	$\frac{1}{2}d$, 1*d*, $1\frac{1}{2}d$, 2*d*, $2\frac{1}{2}d$, 3*d* (*graphite lines*) (*Nos.* 561/6)	60·00	☐
9 Feb. 1959	$4\frac{1}{2}d$ (*No.* 577)	45·00	☐

1967–1989

PRICES for First Day Covers listed below are for stamps, as indicated, used on illustrated envelopes and postmarked with the special First Day of Issue handstamps. Other definitives issued during this period were not accepted for "First Day" treatment by the British Post Office.

£sd Machin Issues

5 June 1967	4*d*, 1s, 1s 9*d* (*Nos.* 731, 742, 744)	1·40	☐
8 Aug. 1967	3*d*, 9*d*, 1s 6*d* (*Nos.* 729, 740, 743)	1·40	☐
5 Feb. 1968	$\frac{1}{2}d$, 1*d*, 2*d*, 6*d* (*Nos.* 723/4, 726, 736)	75	☐
1 July 1968	5*d*, 7*d*, 8*d*, 10*d* (*Nos.* 735, 737/8, 741)	1·10	☐
5 March 1969	2s 6*d*, 5s, 10s, £1 (*Nos.* 787/90)	15·00	☐

Decimal Machin Issues

17 June 1970	10*p*, 20*p*, 50*p*, (*Nos.* 829/31)	5·50	☐
15 Feb. 1971	$\frac{1}{2}p$, 1*p*, $1\frac{1}{2}p$, 2*p*, $2\frac{1}{2}p$, 3*p*, $3\frac{1}{2}p$, 4*p*, 5*p*, 6*p*, $7\frac{1}{2}p$, 9*p* (*Nos.* X841, X844, X848/9, X851, X855, X858, X861, X866, X870, X877, X882) (*Covers carry* "POSTING DELAYED BY THE POST OFFICE STRIKE 1971" *cachet*) ..	2·75	☐
11 Aug. 1971	10*p* (*No.* X885)	1·00	☐

6 Dec. 1972	£1 (*No.* 831*b*)	7·00	☐
24 Oct. 1973	$4\frac{1}{2}p$, $5\frac{1}{2}p$, 8*p* (*Nos.* X865 X868, X878)	1·00	☐
4 Sept. 1974	$6\frac{1}{2}p$ (*No.* X871)	1·10	☐
15 Jan. 1975	7*p* (*No.* X874)	75	☐
24 Sept. 1975	$8\frac{1}{2}p$ (*No.* 881)	1·25	☐
25 Feb. 1976	9*p*, $9\frac{1}{2}p$, 10*p*, $10\frac{1}{2}p$, 11*p*, 20*p* (*Nos.* X883/4, X886, X890, X892, X915)	2·75	☐
2 Feb. 1977	50*p* (*No.* X921)	2·25	☐
2 Feb. 1977	£1, £2, £5 (*Nos.* 1026, 1027/8)	12·00	☐
26 April. 1978	$10\frac{1}{2}p$ (*No.* X891)	1·00	☐
15 Aug. 1979	$11\frac{1}{2}p$, 13*p*, 15*p* (*Nos.* X942, X944, X947)	2·00	☐
30 Jan. 1980	4*p*, 12*p*, $13\frac{1}{2}p$, 17*p*, $17\frac{1}{2}p$, 75*p* (*Nos.* X996, X943, X945, X951, X953, X1018)	4·50	☐
22 Oct. 1980	3*p*, 22*p*, (*Nos.* X930, X962)	1·00	☐
14 Jan. 1981	$2\frac{1}{2}p$, $11\frac{1}{2}p$, 14*p*, $15\frac{1}{2}p$, 18*p*, 25*p* (*Nos.* X929, X893, X946, X948, X954, X970)	2·25	☐
27 Jan. 1982	5*p*, $12\frac{1}{2}p$, $16\frac{1}{2}p$, $19\frac{1}{2}p$, 26*p*, 29*p* (*Nos.* X1004, X898, X950, X957, X971, X978) ..	3·25	☐
30 March 1983	$3\frac{1}{2}p$, 16*p*, 17*p*, $20\frac{1}{2}p$ 23*p*, 28*p*, 31*p* (*Nos.* X931, X949, X952, X961, X965, X975, X981)	6·00	☐
3 Aug. 1983	£1·30 (*No.* 1026*b*)	10·00	☐
28 Aug. 1984	13*p*, 18*p*, 22*p*, 24*p*, 34*p* (*Nos.* X900, X955, X963, X967, X985)	5·00	☐
28 Aug. 1984	£1·33 (*No.* 1026*c*)	8·50	☐
17 Sept. 1985	£1·41 (*No.* 1026*d*)	7·50	☐
29 Oct. 1985	7*p*, 12*p*, (*Nos.* X937, X896)	2·00	☐
2 Sept. 1986	£1·50 (*No.* 1026*e*)	8·00	☐
15 Sept. 1987	£1·60 (*No.* 1026*f*)	8·00	☐
23 Aug. 1988	14*p*, 19*p*, 20*p*, 23*p*, 27*p*, 28*p*, 32*p*, 35*p* (*Nos.* X903, X956, X959, X966, X973, X976, X983, X988)	5·00	☐
26 Sept. 1989	15*p*, 20*p*, 24*p*, 29*p*, 30*p*, 34*p*, 37*p* (*Nos.* X905, X960, X968, X979/80, X986, X990)	3·75	☐
4 Sept. 1990	10*p*, 17*p*, 22*p*, 26*p*, 27*p*, 31*p*, 33*p* (*Nos.* X940, X910, X964, X972, X974, X982, X984) ..	2·75	☐
10 Sept. 1991	6*p*, 18*p*, 24*p*, 28*p*, 34*p*, 35*p*, 39*p* (*Nos.* X936, X913, X969, X977, X987, X989, X991) ..	3·75	☐

For 1989 and 1990 "1st" and "2nd" and 1990 150th Anniversary of the Penny Black first day covers see pages 86/7 and 90.

Keep this Catalogue up to date month by month with —

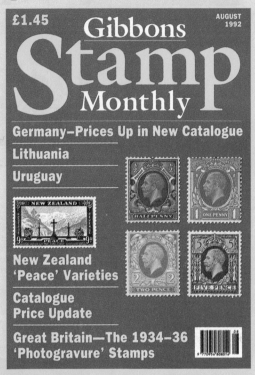

£1.45 — AUGUST 1992

Gibbons Stamp Monthly

Germany—Prices Up in New Catalogue

Lithuania

Uruguay

New Zealand 'Peace' Varieties

Catalogue Price Update

Great Britain—The 1934–36 'Photogravure' Stamps

The only magazine with the Stanley Gibbons Catalogue supplement – and much more besides!

Please send for a FREE COPY and subscription details to:

Hugh Jefferies
Stanley Gibbons Publications Ltd.,
5 Parkside, Christchurch Road,
Ringwood, Hampshire BH24 3SH
Telephone 0425 472363

370 'A Mountain Road'
(T. P. Flanagan)

371 'Deer's Meadow'
(Tom Carr)

372 'Slieve na brock'
(Colin Middleton)

'Ulster '71' Paintings

1971 (16 JUNE) *Two phosphor bands*

881	**370**	3p multicoloured	..	10	10	□	□
882	**371**	7½p multicoloured	..	75	80	□	□
883	**372**	9p multicoloured	..	75	80	□	□
		Set of 3	.. .. ..	1·40	1·50	□	□
		First Day Cover			2·00		□
		Presentation Pack	.. ..	5·00			□

373 John Keats
(150th Death Anniv)

374 Thomas Gray
(Death Bicentenary)

375 Sir Walter Scott
(Birth Bicentenary)

Literary Anniversaries. Events described above

1971 (28 JULY) *Two phosphor bands*

884	**373**	3p black, gold & bl	..	10	10	□	□
885	**374**	5p blk, gold & olive		75	80	□	□
886	**375**	7½p black, gold & brn		75	80	□	□
		Set of 3	.. .. ..	1·40	1·50	□	□
		First Day Cover	.. .. ..		1·60		□
		Presentation Pack	.. ..	5·00			□

376 Servicemen and Nurse
of 1921

377 Roman Centurion

378 Rugby Football, 1871

British Anniversaries. Events described on stamps

1971 (25 AUG.) *Two phosphor bands*

887	**376**	3p multicoloured	..	10	10	□	□
888	**377**	7½p multicoloured	..	75	75	□	□
889	**378**	9p multicoloured	..	75	75	□	□
		Set of 3	.. .. ..	1·40	1·40	□	□
		First Day Cover	.. ..		2·00		□
		Presentation Pack	.. ..	5·00			□

379 Physical Sciences Building,
University College of
Wales, Aberystwyth

380 Faraday Building,
Southampton
University

381 Engineering Department,
Leicester University

382 Hexagon Restaurant,
Essex University

British Architecture (Modern University Buildings)

1971 (22 SEPT.) *Two phosphor bands*

890	**379**	3p multicoloured ..	10	10	☐	☐
891	**380**	5p multicoloured ..	20	25	☐	☐
892	**381**	7½p ochre, black and				
		purple-brown. ..	80	80	☐	☐
893	**382**	9p multicoloured ..	1·60	1·60	☐	☐
		Set of 4	2·50	2·50	☐	☐
		First Day Cover		2·50	☐	
		Presentation Pack	6·00		☐	

Collectors Pack 1971

1971 (29 SEPT.) *Comprises Nos. 835/40 and 881/93*

Collectors Pack	32·00	☐

383 Dream of the Wise Men

384 Adoration of the Magi

385 'Ride of the Magi'

Christmas

1971 (13 OCT.) *Two phosphor bands (3p, 7½p) or one centre phosphor band (2½p)*

894	**383**	2½p multicoloured ..	10	10	☐	☐
895	**384**	3p multicoloured ..	10	10	☐	☐
896	**385**	7½p multicoloured..	90	1·00	☐	☐
		Set of 3	1·00	1·10	☐	☐
		First Day Cover		1·75	☐	
		Presentation Pack	4·50		☐	

386 Sir James Clark Ross

387 Sir Martin Frobisher

388 Henry Hudson

389 Capt. Robert F. Scott

British Polar Explorers

1972 (16 FEB.) *Two phosphor bands*

897	**386**	3p multicoloured ..	10	10	☐	☐
898	**387**	5p multicoloured ..	20	20	☐	☐
899	**388**	7½p multicoloured ..	65	65	☐	☐
900	**389**	9p multicoloured ..	1·10	1·10	☐	☐
		Set of 4	1·75	1·75	☐	☐
		First Day Cover		2·00	☐	
		Presentation Pack	5·00		☐	

390 Statuette of Tutankhamun

391 19th-century Coastguard

392 Ralph Vaughan Williams and Score

Anniversaries. Events described on stamps

1972 (26 APR.) *Two phosphor bands*

901	**390**	3p multicoloured ..	10	10	☐	☐
902	**391**	7½p multicoloured ..	70	80	☐	☐
903	**392**	9p multicoloured ..	70	65	☐	☐
		Set of 3	1·25	1·40	☐	☐
		First Day Cover		2·00	☐	
		Presentation Pack	4·50		☐	

393 St Andrew's, Greensted-juxta-Ongar, Essex

394 All Saints, Earls Barton, Northants

395 St Andrew's, Letheringsett, Norfolk

396 St Andrew's, Helpringham, Lincs

397 St Mary the Virgin, Huish Episcopi, Somerset

British Architecture (Village Churches)

1972 (21 JUNE) *Two phosphor bands*

904	**393**	3p multicoloured ..	10	10	□	□
905	**394**	4p multicoloured ..	20	20	□	□
906	**395**	5p multicoloured ..	20	25	□	□
907	**396**	7½p multicoloured ..	1·00	1·10	□	□
908	**397**	9p multicoloured ..	1·25	1·40	□	□
		Set of 5	2·50	2·75	□	□
		First Day Cover		3·00		□
		Presentation Pack ..	6·00		□	

'Belgica '72' Souvenir Pack

1972 (24 JUNE) *Comprises Nos. 894/6 and 904/8*

	Souvenir Pack	12·00	□

398 Microphones, 1924–69

399 Horn Loudspeaker

400 TV Camera, 1972

401 Oscillator and Spark Transmitter, 1897

Broadcasting Anniversaries. Events described on stamps

1972 (13 SEPT.) *Two phosphor bands*

909	**398**	3p multicoloured ..	10	10	□	□
910	**399**	5p multicoloured ..	15	20	□	□
911	**400**	7½p multicoloured ..	1·00	1·00	□	□
912	**401**	9p multicoloured ..	1·00	1·00	□	□
		Set of 4	2·00	2·00	□	□
		First Day Cover		2·25		□
		Presentation Pack	4·50		□	

402 Angel holding Trumpet

403 Angel playing Lute

404 Angel playing Harp

Christmas

1972 (18 Oct.) *Two phosphor bands (3p, 7½p) or one centre phosphor band (2½p)*

913	402	2½p multicoloured ..	10	15	☐	☐
914	403	3p multicoloured ..	10	15	☐	☐
915	404	7½p multicoloured ..	90	80	☐	☐
		Set of 3	1·00	1·00	☐	☐
		First Day Cover ..		1·40		☐
		Presentation Pack	3·50		☐	

405 Queen Elizabeth II and Prince Philip

406 'Europe'

Royal Silver Wedding

1972 (20 Nov.) *3p 'all-over' phosphor, 20p without phosphor*

916	405	3p brownish black, deep blue and silver	20	20	☐	☐
917		20p brownish black, reddish purple and silver ..	80	80	☐	☐
		Set of 2	1·00	1·00	☐	☐
		First Day Cover		1·25		☐
		Presentation Pack ..	2·50		☐	
		Presentation Pack (Japanese)	4·00		☐	
		Souvenir Book	3·00		☐	
		Gutter Pair (3p)	1·00		☐	
		Traffic Light Gutter Pair (3p)	22·00		☐	

Collectors Pack 1972

1972 (20 Nov.) *Comprises Nos. 897/917*

	Collectors Pack	35·00	☐

Nos. 920/1 were issued horizontally *se-tenant* throughout the sheet.

Britain's Entry into European Communities

1973 (3 Jan.) *Two phosphor bands*

919	406	3p multicoloured ..	10	10	☐	☐
920		5p multicoloured (blue jigsaw) ..	25	35	☐	☐
		a. Pair. Nos. 920/1	1·50	1·60	☐	☐
921		5p multicoloured (green jigsaw) ..	25	35	☐	☐
		Set of 3	1·50	70	☐	☐
		First Day Cover		1·60		☐
		Presentation Pack	3·00		☐	

407 Oak Tree

British Trees (1st issue)

1973 (28 Feb.) *Two phosphor bands*

922	407	9p multicoloured ..	50	45	☐	☐
		First Day Cover		1·00		☐
		Presentation Pack	3·00		☐	

See also No. 949.

408 David Livingstone

409 H. M. Stanley

The above were issued horizontally *se-tenant* throughout the sheet.

410 Sir Francis Drake

411 Sir Walter Raleigh

412 Charles Sturt

41

British Explorers

1973 (18 Apr.) *'All-over' phosphor*

923	**408**	3p multicoloured ..	25	20	☐	☐
		a. *Pair. Nos. 923/4*	1·60	1·75	☐	☐
924	**409**	3p multicoloured ..	25	20	☐	☐
925	**410**	5p multicoloured ..	30	30	☐	☐
926	**411**	7½p multicoloured ..	35	30	☐	☐
927	**412**	9p multicoloured ..	40	40	☐	☐
		Set of 5	2·50	1·25	☐	☐
		First Day Cover		2·50		☐
		Presentation Pack	4·00		☐	

413

414

415

County Cricket 1873–1973

1973 (16 May) *Designs show sketches of W. G. Grace by Harry Furniss. Queen's head in gold. 'All-over' phosphor*

928	**413**	3p black and brown	10	10	☐	☐
929	**414**	7½p black and green	1·25	1·40	☐	☐
930	**415**	9p black and blue	1·50	1·40	☐	☐
		Set of 3	2·50	2·50	☐	☐
		First Day Cover		2·50		☐
		Presentation Pack	3·50		☐	
		Souvenir Book	7·50		☐	
		PHQ Card (No. 928)	50·00	£140	☐	☐

For full information on all future British issues, collectors should write to the British Post Office Philatelic Bureau, 20 Brandon Street, Edinburgh EH3 5TT

416 'Self-portrait' (Sir Joshua Reynolds)

417 'Self-portrait' (Sir Henry Raeburn)

418 'Nelly O'Brien' (Sir Joshua Reynolds)

419 'Rev R. Walker (The Skater)' (Sir Henry Raeburn)

Artistic Anniversaries. *Events described on stamps*

1973 (4 July) *'All-over' phosphor*

931	**416**	3p multicoloured ..	10	10	☐	☐
932	**417**	5p multicoloured ..	20	25	☐	☐
933	**418**	7½p multicoloured ..	70	70	☐	☐
934	**419**	9p multicoloured ..	90	90	☐	☐
		Set of 4	1·60	1·75	☐	☐
		First Day Cover		2·00		☐
		Presentation Pack	3·25		☐	

420 Court Masque Costumes

421 St Paul's Church, Covent Garden

422 Prince's Lodging, Newmarket

423 Court Masque Stage Scene

The 3p and 5p values were printed horizontally *se-tenant* within the sheet.

400th Anniversary of the Birth of Inigo Jones

1973 (15 Aug.) *'All-over' phosphor*

935	420	3p	deep mauve, black and gold ..	10	15	☐ ☐
		a.	Pair. Nos. 935/6	35	40	☐ ☐
936	421	3p	deep brown, black and gold ..	10	15	☐ ☐
937	422	5p	blue, black and gold ..	40	45	☐ ☐
		a.	Pair. Nos. 937/8	1·90	1·50	☐ ☐
938	423	5p	grey-olive, black and gold	40	45	☐ ☐
	Set of 4	.. ..		2·00	1·10	☐ ☐
	First Day Cover				2·00	☐
	Presentation Pack	.. ..		3·50		☐
	PHQ Card (No. 936)			£140	70·00	☐ ☐

424 Palace of Westminster seen from Whitehall

425 Palace of Westminster seen from Millbank

19th Commonwealth Parliamentary Conference

1973 (12 Sept.) *'All-over' phosphor*

939	424	8p	black, grey and pale buff	50	60	☐ ☐
940	425	10p	gold and black	50	40	☐ ☐
	Set of 2	.. ..		1·00	1·00	☐ ☐
	First Day Cover				1·25	☐
	Presentation Pack	.. ..		2·00		☐
	Souvenir Book			8·00		☐
	PHQ Card (No. 939)			40·00	90·00	☐ ☐

426 Princess Anne and Captain Mark Phillips

Royal Wedding

1973 (14 Nov.) *'All-over' phosphor*

941	426	3½p	violet and silver	10	10	☐ ☐
942		20p	brown and silver	90	1·00	☐ ☐
	Set of 2	.. ..		1·00	1·10	☐ ☐
	First Day Cover				1·25	☐
	Presentation Pack	.. ..		2·00		☐
	PHQ Card (No. 941)			10·00	22·00	☐ ☐
	Set of 2 Gutter Pairs ..			6·00		☐
	Set of 2 Traffic Light Gutter Pairs			90·00		☐

427

428

429

430

431

432 'Good King Wenceslas, the Page and Peasant'

The 3p values depict the carol 'Good King Wenceslas' and were printed horizontally *se-tenant* within the sheet.

Christmas

1973 (28 Nov.) *One phosphor band (3p) or 'all-over' phosphor (3½p)*

943	427	3p	multicoloured ..	15	15	☐ ☐
		a.	Strip of 5. Nos. 943/7 ..	3·00	2·75	☐ ☐
944	428	3p	multicoloured ..	15	15	☐ ☐
945	429	3p	multicoloured ..	15	15	☐ ☐
946	430	3p	multicoloured ..	15	15	☐ ☐
947	431	3p	multicoloured ..	15	15	☐ ☐
948	432	3½p	multicoloured ..	15	15	☐ ☐
	Set of 6	.. ..		3·00	80	☐ ☐
	First Day Cover				2·00	☐
	Presentation Pack	.. ..		3·25		☐

Collectors Pack 1973

1973 (28 Nov.) *Comprises Nos.* 919/48

	Collectors Pack	.. .. ..	28·00	☐

Horse Chestnut   Aesculus hippocastanum   **433** Horse Chestnut

43

British Trees (2nd issue)

1974 (27 FEB.) *'All-over' phosphor*

949	**433**	10p multicoloured ..	50	50	☐	☐
		First Day Cover		1·00		☐
		Presentation Pack	2·25		☐	
		PHQ Card	£125	70·00	☐	☐
		Gutter Pair	3·00		☐	
		Traffic Light Gutter Pair	75·00		☐	

434 First Motor Fire-engine, 1904

435 Prize-winning Fire-engine, 1863

436 Steam Fire-engine, 1830

437 Fire-engine, 1766

200th Anniversary of Public Fire Services

1974 (24 APR.) *'All-over' phosphor*

950	**434**	3½p multicoloured ..	10	10	☐	☐
951	**435**	5½p multicoloured ..	25	25	☐	☐
952	**436**	8p multicoloured ..	60	65	☐	☐
953	**437**	10p multicoloured ..	80	85	☐	☐
		Set of 4	1·50	1·60	☐	☐
		First Day Cover		3·00		☐
		Presentation Pack	2·50		☐	
		PHQ Card (No. 950)	£125	60·00	☐	☐
		Set of 4 Gutter Pairs ..	4·00		☐	
		Set of 4 Traffic Light Gutter Pairs	75·00		☐	

438 P & O Packet Peninsular, 1888

439 Farman Biplane, 1911

440 Airmail-blue Van and Postbox, 1930

441 Imperial Airways 'C' Class Flying-boat, 1937

Centenary of Universal Postal Union

1974 (12 JUNE) *'All-over' phosphor*

954	**438**	3½p multicoloured ..	10	10	☐	☐
955	**439**	5½p multicoloured ..	20	25	☐	☐
956	**440**	8p multicoloured ..	30	35	☐	☐
957	**441**	10p multicoloured ..	50	40	☐	☐
		Set of 4	1·00	1·00	☐	☐
		First Day Cover		1·40		☐
		Presentation Pack	2·50		☐	
		Set of 4 Gutter Pairs ..	4·00		☐	
		Set of 4 Traffic Light Gutter Pairs	50·00		☐	

442 Robert the Bruce

443 Owain Glyndŵr

444 Henry the Fifth

445 The Black Prince

Medieval Warriors

1974 (10 JULY) *'All-over' phosphor*

958	**442**	4½p multicoloured ..	10	10	☐	☐
959	**443**	5½p multicoloured ..	20	25	☐	☐
960	**444**	8p multicoloured ..	70	65	☐	☐
961	**445**	10p multicoloured ..	70	70	☐	☐
		Set of 4	1·50	1·50	☐	☐
		First Day Cover		2·50		☐
		Presentation Pack	3·50		☐	
		PHQ Cards (set of 4)	30·00	26·00	☐	☐
		Set of 4 Gutter Pairs ..	6·00		☐	
		Set of 4 Traffic Light Gutter Pairs	80·00		☐	

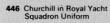

446 Churchill in Royal Yacht Squadron Uniform

447 Prime Minister, 1940

448 Secretary for War and Air, 1919

449 War Correspondent, South Africa, 1899

Birth Centenary of Sir Winston Churchill

1974 (9 Oct.) *Queen's head and inscription in silver. 'All-over' phosphor*

962	**446**	4½p green and blue	15	15	☐	☐
963	**447**	5½p grey and black	20	25	☐	☐
964	**448**	8p rose and lake ..	50	50	☐	☐
965	**449**	10p stone and brown	55	50	☐	☐
	Set of 4		1·25	1·25	☐	☐
	First Day Cover			1·60		☐
	Presentation Pack ..		1·75		☐	
	Souvenir Book ..		2·50		☐	
	PHQ Card (No. 963) ..		8·00	12·00	☐	☐
	Set of 4 Gutter Pairs ..		4·00		☐	
	Set of 4 Traffic Light Gutter Pairs		55·00		☐	

450 'Adoration of the Magi (York Minster, c. 1355)

451 'The Nativity' (St Helen's Church, Norwich, c. 1480)

452 'Virgin and Child' (Ottery St Mary Church, c. 1350)

453 'Virgin and Child' (Worcester Cathedral, c. 1224)

Christmas

1974 (27 Nov.) *Designs show church roof bosses, One phosphor band (3½p) or 'all-over' phosphor (others)*

966	**450**	3½p multicoloured ..	10	10	☐	☐
967	**451**	4½p multicoloured ..	10	10	☐	☐
968	**452**	8p multicoloured ..	45	45	☐	☐
969	**453**	10p multicoloured ..	50	50	☐	☐
	Set of 4		1·00	1·00	☐	☐
	First Day Cover			1·40		☐
	Presentation Pack ..		1·75		☐	
	Set of 4 Gutter Pairs ..		4·00		☐	
	Set of 4 Traffic Light Gutter Pairs		55·00		☐	

Collectors Pack 1974

1974 (27 Nov.) *Comprises Nos 949/69*

	Collectors Pack	11·00	☐

454 Invalid in Wheelchair

Health and Handicap Funds

1975 (22 Jan.) *'All-over' phosphor*

970	**454**	4½p + 1½p azure and blue	25	25	☐	☐
	First Day Cover			1·00		☐
	Gutter Pair		50		☐	
	Traffic Light Gutter Pair		1·00		☐	

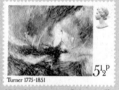

455 'Peace – Burial at Sea'

456 'Snowstorm – Steamer off a Harbour's Mouth'

457 'The Arsenal, Venice'

458 'St Laurent'

Birth Bicentenary of J. M. W. Turner

1975 (19 Feb.) *'All-over' phosphor*

971	**455**	4½p multicoloured ..	10	10	☐	☐
972	**456**	5½p multicoloured ..	15	15	☐	☐
973	**457**	8p multicoloured ..	50	50	☐	☐
974	**458**	10p multicoloured ..	60	60	☐	☐
	Set of 4		1·25	1·25	☐	☐
	First Day Cover			1·50		☐
	Presentation Pack ..		2·50		☐	
	PHQ Card (No. 972) ..		30·00	11·00	☐	☐
	Set of 4 Gutter Pairs ..		2·50		☐	
	Set of 4 Traffic Light Gutter Pairs		8·00		☐	

459 Charlotte Square, Edinburgh

460 The Rows, Chester

The above were printed horizontally *se-tenant* throughout the sheet.

461 Royal Observatory, Greenwich

462 St George's Chapel, Windsor

463 National Theatre, London

European Architectural Heritage Year

1975 (23 APR.) *'All-over' phosphor*

975	**459**	7p multicoloured ..	30	30	☐	☐
		a. *Pair. Nos.* 975/6	90	90	☐	☐
976	**460**	7p multicoloured ..	30	30	☐	☐
977	**461**	8p multicoloured ..	20	25	☐	☐
978	**462**	10p multicoloured ..	25	25	☐	☐
979	**463**	12p multicoloured ..	30	35	☐	☐
		Set of 5 ..	1·50	1·25	☐	
		First Day Cover		2·00		☐
		Presentation Pack ..	3·00		☐	
		PHQ Cards (Nos. 975/7)	7·00	10·00	☐	☐
		Set of 5 Gutter Pairs ..	4·00		☐	
		Set of 5 Traffic Light				
		Gutter Pairs	24·00		☐	

464 Sailing Dinghies

465 Racing Keel Boats

466 Cruising Yachts

467 Multihulls

Sailing

1975 (11 JUNE) *'All-over' phosphor*

980	**464**	7p multicoloured ..	20	20	☐	☐
981	**465**	8p multicoloured ..	30	30	☐	☐
982	**466**	10p multicoloured ..	35	35	☐	☐
983	**467**	12p multicoloured ..	55	55	☐	☐
		Set of 4	1·25	1·25	☐	
		First Day Cover		1·50		☐
		Presentation Pack	1·50		☐	
		PHQ Card (No. 981) ..	4·50	9·00	☐	☐
		Set of 4 Gutter Pairs ..	2·50			
		Set of 4 Traffic Light				
		Gutter Pairs	30·00		☐	

468 Stephenson's Locomotion, 1825

469 *Abbotsford,* 1876

470 *Caerphilly Castle,* 1923

471 High Speed Train, 1975

150th Anniversary of Public Railways

1975 (13 AUG.) *'All-over' phosphor*

984	**468**	7p multicoloured ..	30	35	☐	☐
985	**469**	8p multicoloured ..	30	40	☐	☐
986	**470**	10p multicoloured ..	40	45	☐	☐
987	**471**	12p multicoloured ..	50	60	☐	☐
		Set of 4	1·40	1·60	☐	☐
		First Day Cover		2·50		☐
		Presentation Pack	2·25		☐	
		Souvenir Book	3·00		☐	
		PHQ Cards (set of 4)	60·00	25·00	☐	☐
		Set of 4 Gutter Pairs	3·00		☐	
		Set of 4 Traffic Light				
		Gutter Pairs	14·00		☐	

472 Palace of Westminster

62nd Inter-Parliamentary Union Conference

1975 (3 SEPT.) *'All-over' phosphor*

988	**472**	12p multicoloured ..	50	50	☐	☐
		First Day Cover		1·00		☐
		Presentation Pack	1·25		☐	
		Gutter Pair	1·00		☐	
		Traffic Light Gutter Pair ..	2·00		☐	

473 'Emma and Mr Woodhouse' (*Emma*)

474 'Catherine Morland' (*Northanger Abbey*)

475 'Mr Darcy' (*Pride and Prejudice*)

476 'Mary and Henry Crawford' (*Mansfield Park*)

Birth Bicentenary of Jane Austen (Novelist)

1975 (22 OCT.) *'All-over' phosphor*

989	**473**	8½p multicoloured ..	20	20	☐	☐
990	**474**	10p multicoloured ..	25	25	☐	☐
991	**475**	11p multicoloured ..	40	45	☐	☐
992	**476**	13p multicoloured ..	55	50	☐	☐
		Set of 4	1·25	1·25	☐	☐
		First Day Cover		1·40		☐
		Presentation Pack	2·00		☐	
		PHQ Cards (set of 4)	16·00	15·00	☐	☐
		Set of 4 Gutter Pairs	2·50		☐	
		Set of 4 Traffic Light Gutter Pairs	8·00		☐	

477 Angels with Harp and Lute

478 Angel with Mandolin

479 Angel with Horn

480 Angel with Trumpet

Christmas

1975 (26 NOV.) *One phosphor band (6½p), phosphor-inked (8½p) (background) or 'all-over' phosphor (others)*

993	**477**	6½p multicoloured ..	20	15	☐	☐
994	**478**	8½p multicoloured ..	20	20	☐	☐
995	**479**	11p multicoloured ..	50	50	☐	☐
996	**480**	13p multicoloured ..	50	55	☐	☐
		Set of 4	1·25	1·25	☐	☐
		First Day Cover		1·25		☐
		Presentation Pack	2·00		☐	
		Set of 4 Gutter Pairs	2·50		☐	
		Set of 4 Traffic Light Gutter Pairs	8·00		☐	

Collectors Pack 1975

1975 (26 NOV.) *Comprises Nos. 970/96*

	Collectors Pack	8·00		☐

481 Housewife

482 Policeman

483 District Nurse

484 Industrialist

Telephone Centenary

1976 (10 Mar.) *'All-over' phosphor*

997	**481**	8½p multicoloured ..	20	20	□	□
998	**482**	10p multicoloured ..	25	25	□	□
999	**483**	11p multicoloured ..	40	45	□	□
1000	**484**	13p multicoloured ..	55	50	□	□
		Set of 4	1·25	1·25	□	□
		First Day Cover		1·25		□
		Presentation Pack	2·00		□	
		Set of 4 Gutter Pairs ..	2·50		□	
		Set of 4 Traffic Light				
		Gutter Pairs	8·00		□	

485 Hewing Coal (Thomas Hepburn)
486 Machinery (Robert Owen)

487 Chimney Cleaning (Lord Shaftesbury)
488 Hands clutching Prison Bars (Elizabeth Fry)

Social Reformers

1976 (28 Apr.) *'All-over phosphor*

1001	**485**	8½p multicoloured ..	20	20	□	□
1002	**486**	10p multicoloured ..	25	25	□	□
1003	**487**	11p black, slate-grey and drab	40	50	□	□
1004	**488**	13p slate-grey, black and green	55	45	□	□
		Set of 4	1·25	1·25	□	□
		First Day Cover		1·25		□
		Presentation Pack	2·00		□	
		PHQ Card (No. 1001) ..	5·00	7·50	□	□
		Set of 4 Gutter Pairs	2·50		□	
		Set of 4 Traffic Light				
		Gutter Pairs	8·00		□	

489 Benjamin Franklin (bust by Jean-Jacques Caffieri)

Bicentenary of American Independence

1976 (2 June) *'All-over' phosphor*

1005	**489**	11p multicoloured ..	50	50	□	□
		First Day Cover		1·00		□
		Presentation Pack	1·25		□	
		PHQ Card	4·00	8·50	□	□
		Gutter Pair	1·00		□	
		Traffic Light Gutter Pair ..	2·00		□	

490 'Elizabeth of Glamis'
491 'Grandpa Dickson'

492 'Rosa Mundi'
493 'Sweet Briar'

Centenary of Royal National Rose Society

1976 (30 June) *'All-over' phosphor*

1006	**490**	8½p multicoloured ..	20	20	□	□
1007	**491**	10p multicoloured ..	30	30	□	□
1008	**492**	11p multicoloured ..	45	50	□	□
1009	**493**	13p multicoloured ..	45	40	□	□
		Set of 4	1·25	1·25	□	□
		First Day Cover		1·75		□
		Presentation Pack	2·25		□	
		PHQ Cards (set of 4)	30·00	16·00	□	□
		Set of 4 Gutter Pairs	2·50		□	
		Set of 4 Traffic Light				
		Gutter Pairs	10·00		□	

494 Archdruid
495 Morris Dancing

496 Scots Piper

497 Welsh Harpist

British Cultural Traditions

1976 (4 Aug.) *'All-over' phosphor*

1010	**494**	8½p multicoloured ..	20	20	☐	☐
1011	**495**	10p multicoloured ..	30	30	☐	☐
1012	**496**	11p multicoloured ..	45	50	☐	☐
1013	**497**	13p multicoloured ..	45	40	☐	☐
		Set of 4	1·25	1·25	☐	☐
		First Day Cover		1·25		☐
		Presentation Pack ..	2·00		☐	
		PHQ Cards (set of 4) ..	16·00	9·00	☐	☐
		Set of 4 Gutter Pairs ..	2·50		☐	
		Set of 4 Traffic Light Gutter Pairs	10·00		☐	

498 The Canterbury Tales

499 The Tretyse of Love

500 Game and Playe of Chesse

501 Early Printing Press

500th Anniversary of British Printing

1976 (29 Sept.) *'All-over' phosphor*

1014	**498**	8½p blk, bl & gold	20	20	☐	☐
1015	**499**	10p blk, olive-grn & gold	25	30	☐	☐
1016	**500**	11p blk, grey & gold ..	45	45	☐	☐
1017	**501**	13p brn, ochre & gold ..	50	45	☐	☐
		Set of 4	1·25	1·25	☐	☐
		First Day Cover		1·25		☐
		Presentation Pack ..	2·50		☐	
		PHQ Cards (set of 4) ..	10·00	8·50	☐	☐
		Set of 4 Gutter Pairs ..	2·50		☐	
		Set of 4 Traffic Light Gutter Pairs	8·00		☐	

502 Virgin and Child

503 Angel with Crown

504 Angel appearing to Shepherds

505 The Three Kings

Christmas

1976 (24 Nov.) *Designs show English mediaeval embroidery. One phosphor band (6½p) or 'all-over' phosphor (others)*

1018	**502**	6½p multicoloured ..	15	15	☐	☐
1019	**503**	8½p multicoloured ..	20	20	☐	☐
1020	**504**	11p multicoloured ..	50	50	☐	☐
1021	**505**	13p multicoloured ..	55	55	☐	☐
		Set of 4	1·25	1·25	☐	☐
		First Day Cover		1·25		☐
		Presentation Pack	2·00		☐	
		PHQ Cards (set of 4)	3·00	7·00	☐	☐
		Set of 4 Gutter Pairs ..	2·50		☐	
		Set of 4 Traffic Light Gutter Pairs	8·00		☐	

Collectors Pack 1976

1976 (24 Nov.) *Comprises Nos. 997/1021*

	Collectors Pack	12·00		☐

506 Lawn Tennis

507 Table Tennis

508 Squash

509 Badminton

Racket Sports

1977 (12 Jan.) *Phosphorised paper*

1022	**506**	8½p multicoloured ..	20	20	☐	☐
1023	**507**	10p multicoloured ..	30	30	☐	☐
1024	**508**	11p multicoloured ..	45	50	☐	☐
1025	**509**	13p multicoloured ..	45	40	☐	☐
		Set of 4	1·25	1·25	☐	☐
		First Day Cover		1·50		☐
		Presentation Pack ..	2·00		☐	
		PHQ Cards (set of 4)	8·00	9·50	☐	☐
		Set of 4 Gutter Pairs ..	2·50		☐	
		Set of 4 Traffic Light				
		Gutter Pairs ..	8·00		☐	

510

1977 (2 Feb.)–**87** *Type* 510 *Ordinary paper*

1026	£1 green and olive	3·00	20	☐	☐
1026*b*	£1·30 drab & dp grnish bl ..	8·00	8·00	☐	☐
1026*c*	£1·33 pale mve & grey-blk ..	8·00	8·00	☐	☐
1026*d*	£1·41 drab & dp grnish bl ..	7·50	7·50	☐	☐
1026*e*	£1·50 pale mve & grey-blk ..	6·00	4·00	☐	☐
1026*f*	£1·60 drab and dp grnish bl	6·00	6·00	☐	☐
1027	£2 green and brown ..	5·50	75	☐	☐
1028	£5 pink and blue	13·00	2·00	☐	☐
	Presentation Pack (Nos.				
	1026, 1027/8) ..	22·00		☐	
	Presentation Pack (No.				
	1026f)	12·00		☐	

For First Day Cover prices see page 36.

511 Steroids – Conform-
ational Analysis

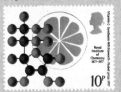

512 Vitamin C –
Synthesis

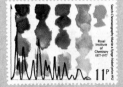

513 Starch –
Chromatography

514 Salt –
Crystallography

Centenary of Royal Institute of Chemistry

1977 (2 Mar.) *'All-over' phosphor*

1029	**511**	8½p multicoloured ..	20	20	☐	☐
1030	**512**	10p multicoloured ..	30	30	☐	☐
1031	**513**	11p multicoloured ..	45	50	☐	☐
1032	**514**	13p multicoloured ..	45	40	☐	☐
		Set of 4	1·25	1·25	☐	☐
		First Day Cover		1·40		☐
		Presentation Pack ..	2·40		☐	
		PHQ Cards (set of 4)	6·00	10·00	☐	☐
		Set of 4 Gutter Pairs ..	2·50		☐	
		Set of 4 Traffic Light				
		Gutter Pairs	8·00		☐	

515

516

517

518

(The designs differ in the decorations of 'ER'.)

Silver Jubilee

1977 (11 May–15 June) *'All-over' phosphor*

1033	**515**	8½p multicoloured ..	20	20	☐	☐
1034		9p mult (15 June) ..	25	25	☐	☐
1035	**516**	10p multicoloured ..	25	30	☐	☐
1036	**517**	11p multicoloured ..	30	35	☐	☐
1037	**518**	13p multicoloured ..	40	40	☐	☐
		Set of 5	1·25	1·40	☐	☐
		First Day Covers (2)		1·75		☐
		Presentation Pack (ex 9p)	2·00		☐	
		Souvenir Book (ex 9p)	4·00		☐	
		PHQ Cards (set of 5)	10·00	8·00	☐	☐
		Set of 5 Gutter Pairs ..	2·75		☐	
		Set of 5 Traffic Light				
		Gutter Pairs	3·75		☐	

519 'Gathering of Nations'

Commonwealth Heads of Government Meeting, London

1977 (8 June) *'All-over' phosphor*

1038	**519**	13p	black, deep green				
			rose and silver ..	50	50	☐	☐
		First Day Cover	.. ..		1·00		☐
		Presentation Pack	.. ..	1·00		☐	
		PHQ Card	.. ..	3·00	3·75	☐	☐
		Gutter Pair	.. ..	1·00		☐	
		Traffic Light Gutter Pair		1·25		☐	

520 Hedgehog

521 Brown Hare

522 Red Squirrel

523 Otter

T **520/4** were printed together, *se-tenant*, throughout the sheet

524 Badger

British Wildlife

1977 (5 Oct.) *'All-over' phosphor*

1039	**520**	9p multicoloured ..	25	20	☐	☐
		a. Strip of 5.				
		Nos. 1039/43 ..	1·75	1·75	☐	☐
1040	**521**	9p multicoloured ..	25	20	☐	☐
1041	**522**	9p multicoloured ..	25	20	☐	☐
1042	**523**	9p multicoloured ..	25	20	☐	☐
1043	**524**	9p multicoloured ..	25	20	☐	☐
		Set of 5	1·75	90	☐	☐
		First Day Cover		2·25		☐
		Presentation Pack	2·25		☐	
		PHQ Cards (set of 5) ..	5·00	5·00	☐	☐
		Gutter Strip of 10	3·75		☐	
		Traffic Light Gutter Strip				
		of 10	4·00		☐	

525 'Three French Hens, Two Turtle Doves and a Partridge in a Pear Tree'

526 'Six Geese a-laying, Five Gold Rings, Four Colly Birds'

527 'Eight Maids a-milking, Seven Swans a-swimming'

528 'Ten Pipers piping, Nine Drummers drumming'

529 'Twelve Lords a-leaping, Eleven Ladies dancing'

530 'A Partridge in a Pear Tree'

T **525/30** depict the carol 'The Twelve Days of Christmas'. T **525/29** were printed horizontally *se-tenant* throughout the sheet.

Christmas

1977 (23 Nov.) *One centre phosphor band (7p) or 'all-over' phosphor (9p)*

1044	**525**	7p multicoloured ..	15	15	☐	☐
		a. Strip of 5				
		Nos. 1044/8 ..	1·00	1·10	☐	☐
1045	**526**	7p multicoloured ..	15	15	☐	☐
1046	**527**	7p multicoloured ..	15	15	☐	☐
1047	**528**	7p multicoloured ..	15	15	☐	☐
1048	**529**	7p multicoloured ..	15	15	☐	☐
1049	**530**	9p multicoloured ..	20	20	☐	☐
		Set of 6	1·10	85	☐	☐
		First Day Cover		1·40		☐
		Presentation Pack	2·00		☐	
		PHQ Cards (set of 6) ..	2·50	4·00	☐	☐
		Set of 6 Gutter Pairs ..	2·50		☐	
		Set of 6 Traffic Light				
		Gutter Pairs	4·50		☐	

Collectors Pack 1977

1977 (23 Nov.) *Comprises Nos.* 1022/5, 1029/49

	Collectors Pack ..	7·00		☐

531 Oil—North Sea
Production Platform

532 Coal—Modern
Pithead

533 Natural Gas—Flame
Rising from Sea

534 Electricity—Nuclear Power
Station and Uranium Atom

Energy Resources

1978 (25 Jan.) *'All-over' phosphor*

1050	**531**	9p multicoloured ..	25	20	☐	☐
1051	**532**	10½p multicoloured ..	25	35	☐	☐
1052	**533**	11p multicoloured ..	35	45	☐	☐
1053	**534**	13p multicoloured ..	55	40	☐	☐
		Set of 4	1·25	1·25	☐	☐
		First Day Cover		1·25		☐
		Presentation Pack	2·00		☐	
		PHQ Cards (set of 4)	3·00	4·00	☐	☐
		Set of 4 Gutter Pairs	2·50		☐	
		Set of 4 Traffic Light				
		Gutter Pairs	4·00		☐	

535 Tower of London

536 Holyroodhouse

537 Caernarvon Castle

538 Hampton Court Palace

British Architecture (Historic Buildings)

1978 (1 Mar.) *'All-over' phosphor*

1054	**535**	9p multicoloured ..	25	20	☐	☐
1055	**536**	10½p. multicoloured ..	25	30	☐	☐
1056	**537**	11p multicoloured ..	45	35	☐	☐
1057	**538**	13p multicoloured ..	50	55	☐	☐
		Set of 4	1·25	1·25	☐	☐
		First Day Cover		1·25		☐
		Presentation Pack	2·00		☐	
		PHQ Cards (set of 4)	2·50	4·00	☐	☐
		Set of 4 Gutter Pairs	2·50	–	☐	
		Set of 4 Traffic Light				
		Gutter Pairs	4·00		☐	
MS1058		121×90 mm. Nos. 1054/57	1·50	1·60	☐	☐
		First Day Cover		2·00		☐

No. **MS**1058 was sold at 53½p, the premium being used for the London 1980 Stamp Exhibition.

539 State Coach

540 St Edward's Crown

541 The Sovereign's Orb

542 Imperial State Crown

25th Anniversary of Coronation

1978 (31 May) *'All-over' phosphor*

1059	**539**	9p gold and blue ..	20	20	☐	☐
1060	**540**	10½p gold and red ..	25	30	☐	☐
1061	**541**	11p gold and green ..	45	50	☐	☐
1062	**542**	13p gold and violet ..	50	40	☐	☐
		Set of 4	1·25	1·25	☐	☐
		First Day Cover		1·25		☐
		Presentation Pack	2·00		☐	
		Souvenir Book	4·00		☐	
		PHQ Cards (set of 4)	2·50	3·00	☐	☐
		Set of 4 Gutter Pairs	2·50		☐	
		Set of 4 Traffic Light				
		Gutter Pairs	4·00		☐	

543 Shire Horse

544 Shetland Pony

545 Welsh Pony

546 Thoroughbred

Horses

1978 (5 JULY) *'All-over' phosphor*

1063	543	9p multicoloured	..	20	25	☐	☐
1064	544	10½p multicoloured	..	25	30	☐	☐
1065	545	11p multicoloured		45	35	☐	☐
1066	546	13p multicoloured	..	50	50	☐	☐
	Set of 4	.. .. ..		1·25	1·25	☐	☐
	First Day Cover	.. ..			1·50		☐
	Presentation Pack	..		2·00		☐	
	PHQ Cards (set of 4)	..		2·50	4·00	☐	☐
	Set of 4 Gutter Pairs	..		2·50		☐	
	Set of 4 Traffic Light						
	Gutter Pairs	.. ..		4·00		☐	

547 Penny-farthing and 1884 Safety Bicycle

548 1920 Touring Bicycles

549 Modern Small-wheel Bicycles

550 1978 Road-racers

Centenaries of Cyclists Touring Club and British Cycling Federation

1978 (2 AUG.) *'All-over' phosphor*

1067	547	9p multicoloured	..	20	20	☐	☐
1068	548	10½p multicoloured	..	25	35	☐	☐
1069	549	11p multicoloured	..	45	45	☐	☐
1070	550	13p multicoloured	..	50	40	☐	☐
	Set of 4	.. .. ..		1·25	1·25	☐	☐
	First Day Cover	.. ..			1·25		☐
	Presentation Pack			2·00		☐	
	PHQ Cards (set of 4)	..		1·50	2·75	☐	☐
	Set of 4 Gutter Pairs			2·50		☐	
	Set of 4 Traffic Light						
	Gutter Pairs	.. ..		4·00		☐	

551 Singing Carols round the Christmas Tree

552 The Waits

553 18th-Century Carol Singers

554 'The Boar's Head Carol'

Christmas

1978 (22 Nov.) *One centre phosphor band (7p) or 'all-over' phosphor (others)*

1071	551	7p multicoloured	..	20	20	☐	☐
1072	552	9p multicoloured	..	25	25	☐	☐
1073	553	11p multicoloured	..	45	50	☐	☐
1074	554	13p multicoloured	..	50	45	☐	☐
	Set of 4	.. .. ..		1·25	1·25	☐	☐
	First Day Cover	.. ..			1·25		☐
	Presentation Pack	..		1·75		☐	
	PHQ Cards (set of 4)	..		1·50	3·50	☐	☐
	Set of 4 Gutter Pairs	..		2·50		☐	
	Set of 4 Traffic Light						
	Gutter Pairs	.. ..		3·00		☐	

Collectors Pack 1978

1978 (22 Nov.) *Comprises Nos. 1050/7, 1059/74*

	Collectors Pack	.. .. ..	7·00	☐

555 Old English Sheepdog

556 Welsh Springer Spaniel

557 West Highland Terrier

558 Irish Setter

Dogs

1979 (7 FEB.) *'All-over' phosphor*

1075 **555**	9p multicoloured		20	25	☐ ☐
1076 **556**	10½p multicoloured		30	35	☐ ☐
1077 **557**	11p multicoloured		45	50	☐ ☐
1078 **558**	13p multicoloured		45	40	☐ ☐
	Set of 4		1·25	1·25	☐ ☐
	First Day Cover			1·50	☐
	Presentation Pack		2·00		☐
	PHQ Cards (set of 4)		3·00	4·00	☐ ☐
	Set of 4 Gutter Pairs		2·50		☐
	Set of 4 Traffic Light				
	Gutter Pairs		3·75		☐

559 Primrose

560 Daffodil

561 Bluebell

562 Snowdrop

Spring Wild Flowers

1979 (21 MAR.) *'All-over' phosphor*

1079 **559**	9p multicoloured		20	20	☐ ☐
1080 **560**	10½p multicoloured		30	35	☐ ☐
1081 **561**	11p multicoloured		45	45	☐ ☐
1082 **562**	13p multicoloured		45	40	☐ ☐
	Set of 4		1·25	1·25	☐ ☐
	First Day Cover			1·50	☐
	Presentation Pack		2·00		☐
	PHQ Cards (set of 4)		1·25	3·50	☐ ☐
	Set of 4 Gutter Pairs		2·50		☐
	Set of 4 Traffic Light				
	Gutter Pairs		3·75		☐

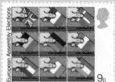

563

564

565

566

T **563/6** show hands placing the flags of the member nations into ballot boxes.

First Direct Elections to European Assembly

1979 (9 MAY) *Phosphorised paper*

1083 **563**	9p multicoloured		20	20	☐ ☐
1084 **564**	10½p multicoloured		30	35	☐ ☐
1085 **565**	11p multicoloured		45	45	☐ ☐
1086 **566**	13p multicoloured		45	40	☐ ☐
	Set of 4		1·25	1·25	☐ ☐
	First Day Cover			1·25	☐
	Presentation Pack		2·00		☐
	PHQ Cards (set of 4)		1·25	3·50	☐ ☐
	Set of 4 Gutter Pairs		2·50		☐
	Set of 4 Traffic Light				
	Gutter Pairs		3·75		☐

Saddling Mahmoud for The Derby 1936

567 'Saddling "Mahmoud" for the Derby, 1936' (Sir Alfred Munnings)

The Liverpool Great National Steeple Chase 1839

568 'The Liverpool Great National Steeple Chase, 1839' (aquatint by F. C. Turner)

The First Spring Meeting, Newmarket 1793

569 'The First Spring Meeting, Newmarket, 1793' (J. N. Sartorius)

Racing at Dorsett Ferry, Windsor 1684

570 'Racing at Dorsett Ferry, Windsor, 1684' (Francis Barlow)

Horseracing Paintings and Bicentenary of The Derby (9p)

1979 (6 June) 'All-over' phosphor

1087	**567**	9p multicoloured ..	25	25	☐	☐
1088	**568**	10½p multicoloured ..	30	30	☐	☐
1089	**569**	11p multicoloured ..	35	50	☐	☐
1090	**570**	13p multicoloured ..	50	55	☐	☐
		Set of 4	1·25	1·40	☐	☐
		First Day Cover		1·50		☐
		Presentation Pack ..	2·00		☐	
		PHQ Cards (set of 4) ..	1·25	3·00	☐	☐
		Set of 4 Gutter Pairs ..	2·50		☐	
		Set of 4 Traffic Light Gutter Pairs	3·75		☐	

571 The Tale of Peter Rabbit (Beatrix Potter)

572 The Wind in the Willows (Kenneth Grahame)

573 Winnie-the-Pooh (A. A. Milne)

574 Alice's Adventures in Wonderland (Lewis Carroll)

T **571/4** depict original illustrations from the four books.

International Year of the Child

1979 (11 July) 'All-over' phosphor

1091	**571**	9p multicoloured ..	45	20	☐	☐
1092	**572**	10½p multicoloured ..	50	35	☐	☐
1093	**573**	11p multicoloured ..	55	40	☐	☐
1094	**574**	13p multicoloured ..	60	55	☐	☐
		Set of 4	1·90	1·40	☐	☐
		First Day Cover		2·00		☐
		Presentation Pack ..	2·25		☐	
		PHQ Cards (set of 4) ..	1·75	2·25	☐	☐
		Set of 4 Gutter Pairs ..	4·00		☐	
		Set of 4 Traffic Light Gutter Pairs	4·75		☐	

For full information on all future British issues, collectors should write to the British Post Office Philatelic Bureau, 20 Brandon Street, Edinburgh EH3 5TT

575 Sir Rowland Hill, 1795–1879

576 General Post, c. 1839

577 London Post, c. 1839

578 Uniform Postage, 1840

Death Centenary of Sir Rowland Hill (Postal Reformer)

1979 (22 Aug.–24 Oct.) 'All-over' phosphor

1095	**575**	10p multicoloured ..	25	25	☐	☐
1096	**576**	11½p multicoloured ..	30	35	☐	☐
1097	**577**	13p multicoloured ..	35	40	☐	☐
1098	**578**	15p multicoloured ..	50	40	☐	☐
		Set of 4	1·25	1·25	☐	☐
		First Day Cover		1·25		☐
		Presentation Pack ..	2·00		☐	
		PHQ Cards (set of 4) ..	1·25	2·25	☐	☐
		Set of 4 Gutter Pairs ..	2·50		☐	
		Set of 4 Traffic Light Gutter Pairs	3·75		☐	
MS1099		89×121 mm. Nos. 1095/8	1·25	1·25	☐	☐
		First Day Cover (24 Oct.) ..		1·25		☐

No. **MS**1099 was sold at 59½p, the premium being used for the London 1980 Stamp Exhibition.

579 Policeman on the Beat

580 Policeman directing Traffic

13ᴾ

15ᴾ

581 Mounted Policewoman **582** River Patrol Boat

150th Anniversary of Metropolitan Police

1979 (26 SEPT.) *Phosphorised paper*

1100	**579**	10p multicoloured ..	25	25	□	□
1101	**580**	11½p multicoloured ..	30	35	□	□
1102	**581**	13p multicoloured ..	35	40	□	□
1103	**582**	15p multicoloured ..	50	40	□	□
		Set of 4	1·25	1·25	□	□
		First Day Cover		1·25		□
		Presentation Pack	2·00		□	
		PHQ Cards (set of 4)	1·25	2·25	□	□
		Set of 4 Gutter Pairs ..	2·50		□	
		Set of 4 Traffic Light				
		Gutter Pairs	3·75		□	

8ᴾ

10ᴾ

583 The Three Kings **584** Angel appearing to the Shepherds

11½ᴾ

13ᴾ

585 The Nativity **586** Mary and Joseph travelling to Bethlehem

15ᴾ

587 The Annunciation

Christmas

1979 (21 Nov.) *One centre phosphor band (8p) or phosphorised paper (others)*

1104	**583**	8p multicoloured ..	20	20	□	□
1105	**584**	10p multicoloured ..	25	25	□	□
1106	**585**	11½p multicoloured ..	30	35	□	□
1107	**586**	13p multicoloured ..	40	40	□	□
1108	**587**	15p multicoloured ..	50	45	□	□
		Set of 5	1·50	1·50	□	□
		First Day Cover		1·50		□
		Presentation Pack	2·25		□	
		PHQ Cards (set of 5)	1·25	2·25	□	□
		Set of 5 Gutter Pairs ..	3·00		□	
		Set of 5 Traffic Light				
		Gutter Pairs	3·75		□	

Collectors Pack 1979

1979 (21 Nov.) *Comprises Nos. 1075/98, 1100/8*

	Collectors Pack	11·00	□

KINGFISHER 10ᴾ

DIPPER 11½ᴾ

588 Kingfisher **589** Dipper

MOORHEN 13ᴾ

YELLOW WAGTAIL 15ᴾ

590 Moorhen **591** Yellow Wagtails

Centenary of Wild Bird Protection Act

1980 (16 JAN.) *Phosphorised paper*

1109	**588**	10p multicoloured ..	25	25	□	□
1110	**589**	11½p multicoloured ..	30	35	□	□
1111	**590**	13p multicoloured ..	55	45	□	□
1112	**591**	15p multicoloured ..	60	50	□	□
		Set of 4	1·50	1·40	□	□
		First Day Cover		1·40		□
		Presentation Pack	2·00		□	
		PHQ Cards (set of 4)	1·25	2·25	□	□
		Set of 4 Gutter Pairs	3·00		□	

592 *Rocket* approaching Moorish Arch, Liverpool

593 First and Second Class Carriages passing through Olive Mount Cutting

594 Third Class Carriage and Cattle Truck crossing Chat Moss

595 Horsebox and Carriage Truck near Bridgewater Canal

596 Goods Truck and Mail-coach at Manchester

T **592/6** were printed together, *se-tenant* in horizontal strips of 5 throughout the sheet.

150th Anniversary of Liverpool and Manchester Railway

1980 (12 MAR.) *Phosphorised paper*

1113	**592**	12p multicoloured ..	25	25	☐	☐
		a. Strip of 5.				
		Nos. 1113/17 ..	1·50	1·60	☐	☐
1114	**593**	12p multicoloured ..	25	25	☐	☐
1115	**594**	12p multicoloured ..	25	25	☐	☐
1116	**595**	12p multicoloured ..	25	25	☐	☐
1117	**596**	12p multicoloured ..	25	25	☐	☐
		Set of 5	1·50	1·10	☐	☐
		First Day Cover		1·60		☐
		Presentation Pack	2·50		☐	
		PHQ Cards (set of 5)	1·25	3·00	☐	☐
		Gutter strip of 10	3·25		☐	

Minimum Price. The minimum price quoted is 10p. This represents a handling charge rather than a basis for valuing common stamps. Where the actual value of a stamp is less than 10p this may be apparent when set prices are shown, particularly for sets including a number of 10p stamps. It therefore follows that in valuing common stamps the 10p catalogue price should not be reckoned automatically since it covers a variation in real scarcity.

597 Montage of London Buildings

"London 1980" International Stamp Exhibition

1980 (9 APR–7 MAY) *Phosphorised paper. Perf* $14\frac{1}{2} \times 14$

1118	**597**	50p agate	1·50	1·50	☐	☐
		First Day Cover		1·50		☐
		Presentation Pack	2·00		☐	
		PHQ Card	50	1·50	☐	☐
		Gutter Pair	3·00		☐	
MS1119		90×123 mm. No. 1118 ..	1·50	1·50	☐	☐
		First Day Cover (7 May)		1·50		☐

No. **MS**1119 was sold at 75p, the premium being used for the exhibition.

598 Buckingham Palace

599 The Albert Memorial

600 Royal Opera House

601 Hampton Court

602 Kensington Palace

London Landmarks

1980 (7 MAY) *Phosphorised paper*

1120	**598**	10½p multicoloured	25	25	□	□
1121	**599**	12p multicoloured	30	30	□	□
1122	**600**	13½p multicoloured	35	35	□	□
1123	**601**	15p multicoloured	50	45	□	□
1124	**602**	17½p multicoloured	60	55	□	□
		Set of 5	1·75	1·75	□	□
		First Day Cover		1·75		□
		Presentation Pack	2·50		□	
		PHQ Cards (set of 5)	1·25	2·50	□	□
		Set of 5 Gutter Pairs	3·50		□	

603 Charlotte Bronte
(*Jane Eyre*)

604 George Eliot (*The Mill on the Floss*)

605 Emily Bronte
(*Wuthering Heights*)

606 Mrs Gaskell (*North and South*)

T **603/6** show authoresses and scenes from their novels. T **603/4** also include the "Europa" C.E.P.T. emblem.

Famous Authoresses

1980 (9 JULY) *Phosphorised paper*

1125	**603**	12p multicoloured	30	30	□	□
1126	**604**	13½p multicoloured	35	35	□	□
1127	**605**	15p multicoloured	40	45	□	□
1128	**606**	17½p multicoloured	60	60	□	□
		Set of 4	1·50	1·50	□	□
		First Day Cover		1·50		□
		Presentation Pack	2·50		□	
		PHQ Cards (set of 4)	1·25	2·00	□	□
		Set of 4 Gutter Pairs	3·00		□	

607 Queen Elizabeth the Queen Mother

80th Birthday of Queen Elizabeth the Queen Mother

1980 (4 AUG.) *Phosphorised paper*

1129	**607**	12p multicoloured	50	50	□	□
		First Day Cover		60		□
		PHQ Card	50	90	□	□
		Gutter Pair	1·00			□

608 Sir Henry Wood

609 Sir Thomas Beecham

610 Sir Malcolm Sargent

611 Sir John Barbirolli

British Conductors

1980 (10 SEPT.) *Phosphorised paper*

1130	**608**	12p multicoloured	30	30	□	□
1131	**609**	13½p multicoloured	35	40	□	□
1132	**610**	15p multicoloured	45	45	□	□
1133	**611**	17½p multicoloured	55	50	□	□
		Set of 4	1·50	1·50	□	□
		First Day Cover		1·50		□
		Presentation Pack	2·00		□	
		PHQ Cards (set of 4)	1·50	2·00	□	□
		Set of 4 Gutter Pairs	3·00		□	

612 Running

613 Rugby

614 Boxing

615 Cricket

618 Apples and Mistletoe

619 Crown, Chains and Bell

620 Holly

Sports Centenaries

1980 (10 Oct.) *Phosphorised paper. Perf* 14 × 14½

1134	**612**	12p multicoloured ..	30	30	☐	☐
1135	**613**	13½p multicoloured ..	35	40	☐	☐
1136	**614**	15p multicoloured ..	40	40	☐	☐
1137	**615**	17½p multicoloured ..	60	55	☐	☐
	Set of 4	1·50	1·50	☐	☐
	First Day Cover		1·50		☐
	Presentation Pack	2·00		☐	
	PHQ Cards (set of 4) ..	1·25	2·00	☐	☐
	Set of 4 Gutter Pairs	3·00		☐	

Centenaries:– 12p Amateur Athletics Association; 13½p Welsh Rugby Union; 15p Amateur Boxing Association; 17½p First England v Australia Test Match.

Christmas

1980 (19 Nov.) *One centre phosphor band* (10p) *or phosphorised paper (others)*

1138	**616**	10p multicoloured ..	25	25	☐	☐
1139	**617**	12p multicoloured ..	30	35	☐	☐
1140	**618**	13½p multicoloured ..	35	40	☐	☐
1141	**619**	15p multicoloured ..	50	45	☐	☐
1142	**620**	17½p multicoloured ..	55	50	☐	☐
	Set of 5	1·75	1·75	☐	☐
	First Day Cover		1·75		☐
	Presentation Pack	2·25		☐	
	PHQ Cards (set of 5) ..	1·25	2·00	☐	☐
	Set of 5 Gutter Pairs	3·50		☐	

Collectors Pack 1980

1980 (19 Nov.) *Comprises Nos.* 1109/18, 1120/42

Collectors Pack	13·00		☐

616 Christmas Tree

617 Candles

621 St. Valentine's Day

622 Morris Dancers

623 Lammastide

624 Medieval Mummers

T **621/22** also include the "Europa" C.E.P.T. emblem.

Folklore

1981 (6 Feb.) *Phosphorised paper*

1143	**621**	14p multicoloured ..	35	35	□	□
1144	**622**	18p multicoloured ..	45	50	□	□
1145	**623**	22p multicoloured ..	60	60	□	□
1146	**624**	25p multicoloured ..	75	70	□	□
		Set of 4	2·00	2·00	□	□
		First Day Cover		2·00		□
		Presentation Pack	2·50		□	
		PHQ Cards (set of 4)	1·50	2·00	□	□
		Set of 4 Gutter Pairs	4·00		□	

625 Blind Man with Guide Dog

626 Hands spelling "Deaf" in Sign Language

627 Disabled Man in Wheelchair

628 Disabled Artist painting with Foot

International Year of the Disabled

1981 (25 Mar.) *Phosphorised paper*

1147	**625**	14p multicoloured ..	35	35	□	□
1148	**626**	18p multicoloured ..	45	50	□	□
1149	**627**	22p multicoloured ..	60	60	□	□
1150	**628**	25p multicoloured ..	75	70	□	□
		Set of 4	2·00	2·00	□	□
		First Day Cover		2·00		□
		Presentation Pack ..	2·50		□	
		PHQ Cards (set of 4)	1·50	2·25	□	□
		Set of 4 Gutter Pairs	4·00		□	

629 *Aglais urticae*

630 *Maculinea arion*

631 *Inachis io*

632 *Carterocephalus palaemon*

Butterflies

1981 (13 May) *Phosphorised paper*

1151	**629**	14p multicoloured ..	35	35	□	□
1152	**630**	18p multicoloured ..	50	50	□	□
1153	**631**	22p multicoloured ..	60	65	□	□
1154	**632**	25p multicoloured ..	70	75	□	□
		Set of 4	2·00	2·00	□	□
		First Day Cover		2·00		□
		Presentation Pack	2·50		□	
		PHQ Cards (set of 4) ..	1·60	2·25	□	□
		Set of 4 Gutter Pairs	4·00		□	

633 Glenfinnan, Scotland

634 Derwentwater, England

635 Stackpole Head, Wales

636 Giant's Causeway, N. Ireland

637 St Kilda, Scotland

50th Anniversary of National Trust for Scotland

1981 (24 JUNE) *Phosphorised paper*

1155	633	14p multicoloured ..	40	40	☐	☐
1156	634	18p multicoloured ..	50	55	☐	☐
1157	635	20p multicoloured ..	55	60	☐	☐
1158	636	22p multicoloured ..	60	60	☐	☐
1159	637	25p multicoloured ..	75	70	☐	☐
		Set of 5	2·50	2·50	☐	☐
		First Day Cover..		2·50		☐
		Presentation Pack	3·25		☐	
		PHQ Cards (set of 5) ..	2·00	2·75	☐	☐
		Set of 5 Gutter Pairs	5·00		☐	

638 Prince Charles and Lady Diana Spencer

Royal Wedding

1981 (22 JULY) *Phosphorised paper*

1160	638	14p multicoloured ..	35	35	☐	☐
1161		25p multicoloured ..	90	90	☐	☐
		Set of 2	1·25	1·25	☐	☐
		First Day Cover		2·25		☐
		Presentation Pack	2·00		☐	
		Souvenir Book	4·50		☐	
		PHQ Cards (set of 2)	1·00	2·00	☐	☐
		Set of 2 Gutter Pairs	2·50		☐	

639 "Expeditions"

640 "Skills"

641 "Service"

642 "Recreation"

25th Anniversary of Duke of Edinburgh Award Scheme

1981 (12 AUG.) *Phosphorised paper. Perf* 14

1162	639	14p multicoloured ..	35	35	☐	☐
1163	640	18p multicoloured ..	50	50	☐	☐
1164	641	22p multicoloured ..	60	60	☐	☐
1165	642	25p multicoloured ..	70	70	☐	☐
		Set of 4	2·00	2·00	☐	☐
		First Day Cover..		2·00		☐
		Presentation Pack	2·50		☐	
		PHQ Cards (set of 4) ..	1·60	2·25	☐	☐
		Set of 4 Gutter Pairs	4·00		☐	

643 Cockle-Dredging

644 Hauling Trawl Net

645 Lobster Potting

646 Hoisting Seine Net

Fishing Industry

1981 (23 SEPT.) *Phosphorised paper*

1166	643	14p multicoloured ..	35	35	☐	☐
1167	644	18p multicoloured ..	50	50	☐	☐
1168	645	22p multicoloured ..	60	60	☐	☐
1169	646	25p multicoloured ..	70	65	☐	☐
		Set of 4	2·00	2·00	☐	☐
		First Day Cover..		2·00		☐
		Presentation Pack	2·50		☐	
		PHQ Cards (set of 4) ..	1·75	2·25	☐	☐
		Set of 4 Gutter Pairs	4·00		☐	

Nos. 1166/9 were issued on the occasion of the centenary of Royal National Mission to Deep Sea Fishermen.

647 Father Christmas

648 Jesus Christ

649 Flying Angel

650 Joseph and Mary arriving at Bethlehem

651 Three Kings approaching Bethlehem

652 Charles Darwin and Giant Tortoises

653 Darwin and Marine Iguanas

654 Darwin, Cactus Ground Finch and Large Ground Finch

655 Darwin and Prehistoric Skulls

Death Centenary of Charles Darwin

1982 (10 FEB.) *Phosphorised paper*

1175	**652**	15½p multicoloured	..	35	35	☐	☐
1176	**653**	19½p multicoloured	..	60	60	☐	☐
1177	**654**	26p multicoloured	..	70	70	☐	☐
1178	**655**	29p multicoloured	..	75	75	☐	☐
		Set of 4	.. .. ..	2·25	2·25	☐	☐
		First Day Cover	.. ..		2·25		☐
		Presentation Pack	..	3·00		☐	
		PHQ Cards (set of 4)	..	2·25	4·50	☐	☐
		Set of 4 Gutter Pairs	..	4·50		☐	

Christmas. Children's Pictures

1981 (18 NOV.) *One phosphor band (11½p) or phosphorised paper (others)*

1170	**647**	11½p multicoloured	..	30	30	☐	☐
1171	**648**	14p multicoloured	..	40	40	☐	☐
1172	**649**	18p multicoloured	..	50	50	☐	☐
1173	**650**	22p multicoloured	..	60	60	☐	☐
1174	**651**	25p multicoloured	..	70	70	☐	☐
		Set of 5	.. .. ..	2·25	2·25	☐	☐
		First Day Cover	.. ..		2·25		☐
		Presentation Pack	.. ..	2·75		☐	
		PHO Cards (set of 5)	.. ..	2·00	2·50	☐	☐
		Set of 5 Gutter Pairs	.. ..	4·50		☐	

Collectors Pack 1981

1981 (18 NOV.) *Comprises Nos. 1143/74*

	Collectors Pack	.. ..	20·00	☐

656 Boys' Brigade

657 Girls' Brigade

658 Boy Scout Movement

659 Girl Guide Movement

For full information on all future British issues, collectors should write to the British Post Office Philatelic Bureau, 20 Brandon Street, Edinburgh EH3 5TT.

Youth Organizations

1982 (24 MAR.) *Phosphorised paper*

1179	656	15½p multicoloured	..	35	35	☐	☐
1180	657	19½p multicoloured		70	70	☐	☐
1181	658	26p multicoloured		90	90	☐	☐
1182	659	29p multicoloured	..	1·00	1·00	☐	☐
		Set of 4	.. ..	2·75	2·75	☐	☐
		First Day Cover	.. .. ..		2·75		☐
		Presentation Pack	.. ..	3·50		☐	
		PHQ Cards (set of 4)	..	2·50	3·00	☐	☐
		Set of 4 Gutter Pairs	..	5·50		☐	

Nos. 1179/82 were issued on the occasion of the 75th anniversary of the Boy Scout Movement, the 125th birth anniversary of Lord Baden-Powell and the centenary of the Boys' Brigade (1983).

660 Ballerina

661 'Harlequin'

662 'Hamlet'

663 Opera Singer

Europa. British Theatre

1982 (28 APR.) *Phosphorised paper*

1183	660	15½p multicoloured	..	35	35	☐	☐
1184	661	19½p multicoloured		70	70	☐	☐
1185	662	26p multicoloured		90	90	☐	☐
1186	663	29p multicoloured	..	1·00	1·00	☐	☐
		Set of 4	.. .. ..	2·75	2·75	☐	☐
		First Day Cover	.. .. ..		2·75		☐
		Presentation Pack	.. ..	3·25		☐	
		PHQ Cards (set of 4)	..	3·00	3·00	☐	☐
		Set of 4 Gutter Pairs	..	5·50		☐	

664 Henry VIII and *Mary Rose*

665 Admiral Blake and *Triumph*

666 Lord Nelson and HMS *Victory*

667 Lord Fisher and HMS *Dreadnought*

668 Viscount Cunningham and HMS *Warspite*

Maritime Heritage

1982 (16 JUNE) *Phosphorised paper*

1187	664	15½p multicoloured	..	35	35	☐	☐
1188	665	19½p multicoloured	..	60	60	☐	☐
1189	666	24p multicoloured	..	70	70	☐	☐
1190	667	26p multicoloured	..	80	80	☐	☐
1191	668	29p multicoloured	..	90	90	☐	☐
		Set of 5	.. ..	3·00	3·00	☐	☐
		First Day Cover	.. .. ..		3·00		☐
		Presentation Pack	.. ..	3·50		☐	
		PHQ Cards (set of 5)	..	3·50	3·50	☐	☐
		Set of 5 Gutter Pairs	.. ..	6·00		☐	

669 "Strawberry Thief" (William Morris)

670 Untitled (Steiner and Co)

671 "Cherry Orchard"
(Paul Nash)

672 "Chevron" (Andrew
Foster)

British Textiles

1982 (23 JULY) *Phosphorised paper*

1192	**669**	15½p multicoloured ..	35	35	☐	☐
1193	**670**	19½p multicoloured ..	70	70	☐	☐
1194	**671**	26p multicoloured ..	70	70	☐	☐
1195	**672**	29p multicoloured ..	1·00	1·00	☐	☐
		Set of 4	2·50	2·50	☐	☐
		First Day Cover		2·50		☐
		Presentation Pack ..	3·25		☐	
		PHQ Cards .(set of 4) ..	3·00	3·50	☐	☐
		Set of 4 Gutter Pairs ..	5·00		☐	

Nos 1192/5 were issued on the occasion of the 250th birth anniversary of Sir Richard Arkwright (inventor of spinning machine).

673 Development of Communications

674 Modern Technological Aids

Information Technology

1982 (8 SEPT.) *Phosphorised paper. Perf* 14 × 15

1196	**673**	15½p multicoloured ..	45	50	☐	☐
1197	**674**	26p multicoloured ..	80	85	☐	☐
		Set of 2	1·25	1·25	☐	☐
		First Day Cover		1·50		☐
		Presentation Pack ..	2·00		☐	
		PHQ Cards (set of 2) ..	1·50	3·50	☐	☐
		Set of 2 Gutter Pairs ..	2·50		☐	

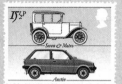

675 Austin "Seven" and "Metro" **676** Ford "Model T" and "Escort"

677 Jaguar "SS1" and "XJ6" **678** Rolls-Royce "Silver Ghost"
and "Silver Spirit"

British Motor Industry

1982 (13 OCT.) *Phosphorised paper. Perf* 14½ × 14

1198	**675**	15½p multicoloured ..	50	50	☐	☐
1199	**676**	19½p multicoloured ..	1·00	1·10	☐	☐
1200	**677**	26p multicoloured ..	1·10	1·25	☐	☐
1201	**678**	29p multicoloured ..	1·25	1·40	☐	☐
		Set of 4	3·50	3·75	☐	☐
		First Day Cover		3·75		☐
		Presentation Pack	4·25		☐	
		PHQ Cards (set of 4)	2·75	4·50	☐	☐
		Set of 4 Gutter Pairs	7·00		☐	

679 "While Shepherds Watched" **680** "The Holly and the Ivy"

681 "I Saw Three Ships" **682** "We Three Kings"

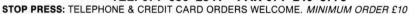

683 "Good King Wenceslas"

Christmas. Carols

1982 (17 Nov.) *One phosphor band* (12½p) *or phosphorised paper* (*others*)

1202	**679**	12½p multicoloured	..	30	30	☐ ☐
1203	**680**	15½p multicoloured		55	55	☐ ☐
1204	**681**	19½p multicoloured		80	80	☐ ☐
1205	**682**	26p multicoloured		80	80	☐ ☐
1206	**683**	29p multicoloured		90	90	☐ ☐
		Set of 5		3·00	3·00	☐ ☐
		First Day Cover			3·00	☐
		Presentation Pack ..		3·50		☐
		PHQ Cards (set of 5) ..		2·75	4·50	☐ ☐
		Set of 5 Gutter Pairs ..		6·00		☐

Collectors Pack 1982

1982 (17 Nov.) *Comprises Nos.* 1175/1206

	Collectors Pack		27·00	☐

684 Salmon

685 Pike

686 Trout   **687** Perch

British River Fishes

1983 (26 Jan.) *Phosphorised paper*

1207	**684**	15½p multicoloured	..	35	35	☐ ☐
1208	**685**	19½p multicoloured		70	70	☐ ☐
1209	**686**	26p multicoloured		80	80	☐ ☐
1210	**687**	29p multicoloured		90	90	☐ ☐
		Set of 4		2·50	2·50	☐ ☐
		First Day Cover			2·75	☐
		Presentation Pack ..		3·25		☐
		PHQ Cards (set of 4) ..		2·50	5·00	☐ ☐
		Set of 4 Gutter Pairs ..		5·00		☐

688 Tropical Island   **689** Desert

690 Temperate Farmland   **691** Mountain Range

Commonwealth Day. Geographical Regions

1983 (9 Mar.) *Phosphorised paper*

1211	**688**	15½p multicoloured	..	35	35	☐ ☐
1212	**689**	19½p multicoloured		70	70	☐ ☐
1213	**690**	26p multicoloured		80	80	☐ ☐
1214	**691**	29p multicoloured		90	90	☐ ☐
		Set of 4		2·50	2·50	☐ ☐
		First Day Cover			2·50	☐
		Presentation Pack ..		3·25		☐
		PHQ Cards (set of 4) ..		2·50	4·50	☐ ☐
		Set of 4 Gutter Pairs ..		5·00		☐

692 Humber Bridge   **693** Thames Flood Barrier

694 *Iolair* (oilfield emergency support vessel)

Europa. Engineering Achievements

1983 (25 MAY) *Phosphorised paper.*

1215	**692**	16p multicoloured	..	55	55	☐	☐
1216	**693**	20½p multicoloured	..	1·25	1·25	☐	☐
1217	**694**	28p multicoloured	..	1·25	1·25	☐	☐
		Set of 3		2·75	2·75	☐	☐
		First Day Cover			2·75		☐
		Presentation Pack		3·50		☐	
		PHQ Cards (set of 3) ..		2·50	3·75	☐	☐
		Set of 3 Gutter Pairs		5·50		☐	

British Army Uniforms

1983 (6 JULY) *Phosphorised paper.*

1218	**695**	16p multicoloured	..	40	40	☐	☐
1219	**696**	20½p multicoloured	..	70	70	☐	☐
1220	**697**	26p multicoloured	..	80	80	☐	☐
1221	**698**	28p multicoloured	..	80	80	☐	☐
1222	**699**	31p multicoloured	..	90	90	☐	☐
		Set of 5		3·25	3·25	☐	☐
		First Day Cover			3·50		☐
		Presentation Pack		4·25		☐	
		PHQ Cards (set of 5) ..		4·00	5·00	☐	☐
		Set of 5 Gutter Pairs ..		6·50		☐	

Nos. 1218/22 were issued on the occasion of the 350th anniversary of The Royal Scots, the senior line regiment of the British Army.

695 Musketeer and Pikeman. The Royal Scots (1633)

696 Fusilier and Ensign. The Royal Welch Fusiliers (mid-18th century)

700 20th-Century Garden, Sissinghurst

701 19th-Century Garden, Biddulph Grange

697 Riflemen. 96th Rifles (The Royal Green Jackets) (1805)

698 Sergeant (khaki service uniform) and Guardsman (full dress). The Irish Guards (1900)

702 18th-Century Garden, Blenheim

703 17th-Century Garden, Pitmedden

699 Paratroopers. The Parachute Regiment (1983)

British Gardens

1983 (24 AUG.) *Phosphorised paper. Perf 14*

1223	**700**	16p multicoloured	..	50	40	☐	☐
1224	**701**	20½p multicoloured	..	60	65	☐	☐
1225	**702**	28p multicoloured	..	95	1·00	☐	☐
1226	**703**	31p multicoloured	..	1·00	1·00	☐	☐
		Set of 4		2·75	2·75	☐	☐
		First Day Cover			2·75		☐
		Presentation Pack		3·50		☐	
		PHQ Cards (set of 4)		3·00	4·50	☐	☐
		Set of 4 Gutter Pairs		5·50		☐	

704 Merry-go-round

705 Big Wheel, Helter-skelter and Performing Animals

706 Side-shows

707 Early Produce Fair

British Fairs

1983 (5 OCT.) *Phosphorised paper.*

1227	**704**	16p multicoloured	..	50	40	☐	☐
1228	**705**	20½p multicoloured	..	60	65	☐	☐
1229	**706**	28p multicoloured	..	95	1·00	☐	☐
1230	**707**	31p multicoloured	..	1·00	1·00	☐	☐
	Set of 4	.. .. ..	..	2·75	2·75	☐	☐
	First Day Cover	.. ..	..		2·75		☐
	Presentation Pack	.. ..	..	3·50		☐	
	PHQ Cards (set of 4)	..	..	3·00	4·50	☐	☐
	Set of 4 Gutter Pairs	..	..	5·50		☐	

Nos. 1227/30 were issued to mark the 850th Anniversary of St. Bartholomew's Fair, Smithfield, London.

708 "Christmas Post" (pillar-box)

709 "The Three Kings" (chimney-pots)

710 "World at Peace" (Dove and Blackbird)

711 "Light of Christmas" (street lamp)

712 "Christmas Dove" (hedge sculpture)

Christmas

1983 (16 Nov.) *One phosphor band (12½p) or phosphorised paper (others)*

1231	**708**	12½p multicoloured	..	30	30	☐	☐
1232	**709**	16p multicoloured	..	45	45	☐	☐
1233	**710**	20½p multicoloured	..	70	70	☐	☐
1234	**711**	28p multicoloured	..	90	90	☐	☐
1235	**712**	31p multicoloured	..	1·00	1·00	☐	☐
	Set of 5	.. .. ..	..	3·00	3·00	☐	☐
	First Day Cover	.. ..			3·00		☐
	Presentation Pack ..	..		3·50		☐	
	PHQ Cards (set of 5)	..	..	3·00	4·50	☐	☐
	Set of 5 Gutter Pairs	..	..	6·00		☐	

Collectors Pack 1983

1983 (16 Nov.) *Comprises Nos. 1207/35*

	Collectors Pack	.. ..	45·00	☐

713 Arms of the College of Arms

714 Arms of King Richard III (founder)

715 Arms of the Earl Marshal of England

716 Arms of the City of London

500th Anniversary of College of Arms

1984 (17 Jan) *Phosphorised paper. Perf* 14½

1236	**713**	16p multicoloured	..	40	40	☐	☐
1237	**714**	20½p multicoloured	..	70	70	☐	☐
1238	**715**	28p multicoloured	..	1·00	1·00	☐	☐
1239	**716**	31p multicoloured	..	1·25	1·25	☐	☐
		Set of 4	.. .. ..	3·00	3·00	☐	☐
		First Day Cover	.. .. ..		3·00		☐
		Presentation Pack	.. ..	3·50		☐	
		PHQ Cards (set of 4)	.. ..	2·50	5·00	☐	☐
		Set of 4 Gutter Pairs	..	6·00		☐	

717 Highland Cow

718 Chillingham Wild Bull

719 Hereford Bull

720 Welsh Black Bull

721 Irish Moiled Cow

British Cattle

1984 (6 Mar.) *Phosphorised paper.*

1240	**717**	16p multicoloured	..	40	40	☐	☐
1241	**718**	20½p multicoloured	..	65	65	☐	☐
1242	**719**	26p multicoloured	..	70	70	☐	☐
1243	**720**	28p multicoloured	..	85	85	☐	☐
1244	**721**	31p multicoloured	..	1·00	1·00	☐	☐
		Set of 5	.. ..	3·25	3·25	☐	☐
		First Day Cover	.. ..		3·50		☐
		Presentation Pack	.. ..	4·25		☐	
		PHQ Cards (set of 5)	.. ..	3·00	5·00	☐	☐
		Set of 5 Gutter Pairs	.. ..	6·50		☐	

Nos. 1240/4 marked the centenary of the Highland Cattle Society and the bicentenary of the Royal Highland and Agricultural Society of Scotland.

722 Festival Hall, Liverpool

723 Milburngate Shopping Centre, Durham

724 Bush House, Bristol

725 Commercial Street Housing Scheme, Perth

Urban Renewal

1984 (10 Apr.) *Phosphorised paper.*

1245	**722**	16p multicoloured	..	40	40	☐	☐
1246	**723**	20½p multicoloured	..	70	70	☐	☐
1247	**724**	28p multicoloured	..	95	95	☐	☐
1248	**725**	31p multicoloured	..	1·00	1·00	☐	☐
		Set of 4	.. ..	2·75	2·75	☐	☐
		First Day Cover	.. ..		3·00		☐
		Presentation Pack	.. ..	3·50		☐	
		PHQ Cards (set of 4)	.. ..	2·50	5·00	☐	☐
		Set of 4 Gutter Pairs	..	5·50		☐	

Nos. 1245/8 mark the opening of the International Gardens Festival, Liverpool, and the 150th anniversaries of the Royal Institute of British Architects and the Chartered Institute of Building.

726 C.E.P.T. 25th Anniversary Logo

727 Abduction of Europa

Nos. 1249/50 and 1251/2 were each printed together, *se-tenant*, in horizontal pairs throughout the sheets.

Europa. 25th Anniversary of C.E.P.T. and 2nd European Parliamentary Elections

1984 (15 MAY) *Phosphorised paper.*

1249	**726**	16p greenish slate, dp blue and gold ..	60	60	☐	☐
		a. *Horiz pair. Nos.* 1249/50 ..	1·25	1·25	☐	☐
1250	**727**	16p greenish slate, dp bl, blk and gold ..	60	60	☐	☐
1251	**726**	20½p Venetian red, deep magenta and gold ..	1·00	1·00	☐	☐
		a. *Horizontal pair. Nos.* 1251/2 ..	2·00	2·00	☐	☐
1252	**727**	20½p Venetian red, deep magenta, black and gold ..	1·00	1·00	☐	☐
		Set of 4	3·00	3·00	☐	☐
		First Day Cover		3·00		☐
		Presentation Pack ..	4·25		☐	
		PHQ Cards (set of 4) ..	2·50	5·00	☐	☐
		Set of 4 Gutter Pairs ..	6·00		☐	

728 Lancaster House

London Economic Summit Conference

1984 (5 JUNE) *Phosphorised paper.*

1253	**728**	31p multicoloured ..	1·25	1·25	☐	☐
		First Day Cover		2·25		☐
		PHQ Card	50	1·75	☐	☐
		Gutter Pair	2·50		☐	

729 View of Earth from "Apollo 11"

730 Navigational Chart of English Channel

731 Greenwich Observatory

732 Sir George Airey's Transit Telescope

Centenary of Greenwich Meridian

1984 (26 JUNE) *Phosphorised paper. Perf* $14 \times 14\frac{1}{2}$

1254	**729**	16p multicoloured ..	40	40	☐	☐
1255	**730**	20½p multicoloured ..	65	65	☐	☐
1256	**731**	28p multicoloured ..	1·10	1·10	☐	☐
1257	**732**	31p multicoloured ..	1·25	1·25	☐	☐
		Set of 4	3·00	3·00	☐	☐
		First Day Cover		3·00		☐
		Presentation Pack ..	3·75		☐	
		PHQ Cards (set of 4) ..	2·50	5·50	☐	☐
		Set of 4 Gutter Pairs ..	6·00		☐	

733 Bath Mail Coach, 1784

734 Attack on Exeter Mail, 1816

735 Norwich Mail in Thunderstorm, 1827

736 Holyhead and Liverpool Mails leaving London, 1828

737 Edinburgh Mail Snowbound, 1831

T **733/7** were printed together, *se-tenant* in horizontal strips of 5 throughout the sheet.

Bicentenary of First Mail Coach Run, Bath and Bristol to London

1984 (31 JULY) *Phosphorised paper*

1258	**733**	16p multicoloured	..	65	65	☐	☐
		a. *Horiz strip of 5.*					
		Nos. 1258/62	..	3·00	3·00	☐	☐
1259	**734**	16p multicoloured	..	65	65	☐	☐
1260	**735**	16p multicoloured	..	65	65	☐	☐
1261	**736**	16p multicoloured	..	65	65	☐	☐
1262	**737**	16p multicoloured	..	65	65	☐	☐
		Set of 5		3·00	3·00	☐	☐
		First Day Cover			3·00		☐
		Presentation Pack		3·75		☐	
		Souvenir Book		6·00		☐	
		PHQ Cards (set of 5) ..		3·00	5·00	☐	☐
		Gutter Strip of 10		6·00		☐	

738 Nigerian Clinic

739 Violinist and Acropolis, Athens

740 Building Project, Sri Lanka

741 British Council Library

50th Anniversary of The British Council

1984 (25 SEPT.) *Phosphorised paper*

1263	**738**	17p multicoloured	..	50	50	☐	☐
1264	**739**	22p multicoloured	..	75	75	☐	☐
1265	**740**	31p multicoloured	..	1·10	1·10	☐	☐
1266	**741**	34p multicoloured	..	1·25	1·25	☐	☐
		Set of 4		3·25	3·25	☐	☐
		First Day Cover		..	3·50		☐
		Presentation Pack ..		4·00		☐	
		PHQ Cards (set of 4) ..		3·00	4·50	☐	☐
		Set of 4 Gutter Pairs ..		6·50		☐	

For full information on all future British issues, collectors should write to the British Post Office Philatelic Bureau, 20 Brandon Street, Edinburgh EH3 5TT.

742 The Holy Family

743 Arrival in Bethlehem

744 Shepherd and Lamb

745 Virgin and Child

746 Offering of Frankincense

Christmas

1984 (20 Nov.) *One phosphor band (13p) or phosphorised paper (others)*

1267	**742**	13p multicoloured	..	30	30	☐	☐
1268	**743**	17p multicoloured	..	50	50	☐	☐
1269	**744**	22p multicoloured	..	70	70	☐	☐
1270	**745**	31p multicoloured	..	1·10	1·10	☐	☐
1271	**746**	34p multicoloured	..	1·25	1·25	☐	☐
		Set of 5		3·50	3·50	☐	☐
		First Day Cover			3·50		☐
		Presentation Pack		4·00		☐	
		PHQ Cards (set of 5)		3·00	4·50	☐	☐
		Set of 5 Gutter Pairs		7·00		☐	

Collectors Pack 1984

1984 (20 Nov.) *Comprises Nos. 1236/71*

Collectors Pack	45·00		☐

Post Office Yearbook

1984 *Comprises Nos. 1236/71 in hardbound book with slip case.*

Yearbook	£110		☐

747 "The Flying Scotsman"

748 "The Golden Arrow"

749 "The Cheltenham Flyer"

750 "The Royal Scot"

751 "The Cornish Riviera"

Famous Trains

1985 (22 JAN.) *Phosphorised paper*

1272	747	17p multicoloured	..	60	60	☐	☐
1273	748	22p multicoloured	..	90	90	☐	☐
1274	749	29p multicoloured	..	1·25	1·25	☐	☐
1275	750	31p multicoloured	..	1·25	1·25	☐	☐
1276	751	34p multicoloured	..	1·60	1·60	☐	☐
		Set of 5		5·00	5·00	☐	☐
		First Day Cover			6·00	☐	
		Presentation Pack		7·50		☐	
		PHQ Cards (set of 5)		3·50	11·00	☐	☐
		Set of 5 Gutter Pairs		10·00		☐	

Nos. 1272/6 were issued on the occasion of the 150th anniversary of the Great Western Railway Company.

752 *Bombus terrestris* (bee)

753 *Coccinella septempunctata* (ladybird)

754 *Decticus verrucivorus* (bush-cricket)

755 *Lucanus cervus* (stag beetle)

756 *Anax imperator* (dragonfly)

Insects

1985 (12 MARCH) *Phosphorised paper*

1277	752	17p multicoloured	..	50	55	☐	☐
1278	753	22p multicoloured	..	70	70	☐	☐
1279	754	29p multicoloured	..	90	90	☐	☐
1280	755	31p multicoloured	..	1·10	1·10	☐	☐
1281	756	34p multicoloured	..	1·10	1·10	☐	☐
		Set of 5		4·00	4·00	☐	☐
		First Day Cover			4·25	☐	
		Presentation Pack		5·00		☐	
		PHQ Cards (set of 5)		3·00	5·50	☐	☐
		Set of 5 Gutter Pairs		8·00		☐	

Nos. 1277/81 were issued on the occasion of the centenaries of the Royal Entomological Society of London's Royal Charter and of the Selborne Society.

757 "Water Music", by Handel

758 "The Planets", by Holst

THIRTY·ONE·PENCE

THE·FIRST·CUCKOO
Frederick Delius

759 "The First Cuckoo", by Delius

THIRTY·FOUR·PENCE

SEA·PICTURES
Edward Elgar

760 "Sea Pictures", by Elgar

Europa – European Music Year

1985 (14 May) *Phosphorised paper. Perf* 14½

1282	**757**	17p multicoloured	..	75	75	☐	☐
1283	**758**	22p multicoloured	..	1·00	1·00	☐	☐
1284	**759**	31p multicoloured	..	1·40	1·40	☐	☐
1285	**760**	34p multicoloured	..	1·60	1·60	☐	☐
		Set of 4	..	4·25	4·25	☐	☐
		First Day Cover ..	..		4·25		☐
		Presentation Pack ..	..	5·00		☐	
		PHQ Cards (set of 4)	..	2·50	5·25	☐	☐
		Set of 4 Gutter Pairs	..	8·00		☐	

Nos. 1282/5 were issued on the occasion of the 300th birth anniversary of Handel.

761 R.N.L.I. Lifeboat and Signal Flags

762 Beachy Head Lighthouse and Chart

763 "Marecs A" Communications Satellite and Dish Aerials

764 Buoys

Safety at Sea

1985 (18 June) *Phosphorised paper. Perf* 14

1286	**761**	17p multicoloured	..	50	50	☐	☐
1287	**762**	22p multicoloured	..	75	75	☐	☐
1288	**763**	31p multicoloured	..	1·10	1·10	☐	☐
1289	**764**	34p multicoloured	..	1·25	1·25	☐	☐
		Set of 4	..	3·25	3·25	☐	☐
		First Day Cover ..	..		4·00		☐
		Presentation Pack ..	..	4·25		☐	
		PHQ Cards (set of 4)	..	2·50	5·25	☐	☐
		Set of 4 Gutter Pairs	..	6·50		☐	

Nos. 1286/9 were issued on the occasion of the bicentenary of the unimmersible lifeboat and the 50th anniversary of Radar.

765 Datapost Motorcyclist, City of London

766 Rural Postbus

767 Parcel Delivery in Winter

768 Town Letter Delivery

350 Years of Royal Mail Public Postal Service

1985 (30 July) *Phosphorised paper*

1290	**765**	17p multicoloured	..	50	50	☐	☐
1291	**766**	22p multicoloured	..	75	75	☐	☐
1292	**767**	31p multicoloured	..	1·10	1·10	☐	☐
1293	**768**	34p multicoloured	..	1·25	1·25	☐	☐
		Set of 4	..	3·25	3·25	☐	☐
		First Day Cover ..	..		4·00		☐
		Presentation Pack ..	..	4·25		☐	
		PHQ Cards (set of 4)	..	3·00	5·25	☐	☐
		Set of 4 Gutter Pairs	..	6·50		☐	

769 King Arthur and Merlin

770 The Lady of the Lake

771 Queen Guinevere and
Sir Lancelot

772 Sir Galahad

777 Alfred Hitchcock (from
photo by Howard Coster)

Arthurian Legends

1985 (3 SEPT.) *Phosphorised paper*

1294	**769**	17p multicoloured	..	50	50	☐	☐
1295	**770**	22p multicoloured	..	75	75	☐	☐
1296	**771**	31p multicoloured	..	1·25	1·25	☐	☐
1297	**772**	34p multicoloured	..	1·40	1·40	☐	☐
		Set of 4	.. ..	3·50	3·50	☐	☐
		First Day Cover	.. .. ..		4·00		☐
		Presentation Pack	..	4·75		☐	
		PHQ Cards (set of 4)	.. ..	3·00	5·25	☐	☐
		Set of 4 Gutter Pairs	..	7·00		☐	

Nos. 1294/7 were issued on the occasion of the 500th anniversary of the printing of Sir Thomas Malory's *Morte d'Arthur*.

British Film Year

1985 (8 OCT.) *Phosphorised paper. Perf* 14½

1298	**773**	17p multicoloured	..	50	50	☐	☐
1299	**774**	22p multicoloured	..	85	90	☐	☐
1300	**775**	29p multicoloured	..	1·40	1·40	☐	☐
1301	**776**	31p multicoloured	..	1·40	1·40	☐	☐
1302	**777**	34p multicoloured	..	1·40	1·40	☐	☐
		Set of 5	.. ..	5·00	5·00	☐	☐
		First Day Cover	.. ..		5·25		☐
		Presentation Pack	.. ..	6·00		☐	
		Souvenir Book	.. ..	7·00		☐	
		PHQ Cards (set of 5)	.. ..	3·25	5·75	☐	☐
		Set of 5 Gutter Pairs	.. ..	10·00		☐	

773 Peter Sellers (from photo
by Bill Brandt)

774 David Niven (from photo
by Cornell Lucas)

775 Charlie Chaplin (from photo
by Lord Snowdon)

776 Vivien Leigh (from photo
by Angus McBean)

778 Principal Boy

779 Genie

780 Dame

781 Good Fairy

782 Pantomime Cat

Christmas. Pantomime Characters

1985 (19 Nov.) *One phosphor band (12p) or phosphorised paper (others)*

1303	**778**	12p multicoloured	..	45	45 □ □
1304	**779**	17p multicoloured	..	55	55 □ □
1305	**780**	22p multicoloured	..	85	85 □ □
1306	**781**	31p multicoloured	..	1·10	1·10 □ □
1307	**782**	34p multicoloured	..	1·25	1·25 □ □
		Set of 5 ..	.. .. ..	3·75	3·75 □ □
		First Day Cover ..	.. ..		4·00 □
		Presentation Pack ..	..	4·50	□
		PHQ Cards (Set of 5)	..	3·00	5·50 □ □
		Set of 5 Gutter Pairs	..	7·50	□

Collectors Pack 1985

1985 (19 Nov.) *Comprises Nos. 1272/1307*

	Collectors Pack	.. .. ..	45·00 □

Post Office Yearbook

1985 *Comprises Nos. 1272/1307 in hardbound book with slip case.*

	Yearbook	.. .. ..	85·00 □

783 Light Bulb and North Sea Oil Drilling Rig (Energy)

784 Thermometer and Pharmaceutical Laboratory (Health)

785 Garden Hoe and Steel Works (Steel)

786 Loaf of Bread and Cornfield (Agriculture)

Industry Year

1986 (14 Jan.) *Phosphorised paper. Perf 14½ × 14*

1308	**783**	17p multicoloured	..	45	45 □ □
1309	**784**	22p multicoloured	..	70	70 □ □
1310	**785**	31p multicoloured	..	1·10	1·10 □ □
1311	**786**	34p multicoloured	..	1·10	1·10 □ □
		Set of 4 ..	.. .. ..	3·00	3·00 □ □
		First Day Cover ..	..		4·50 □
		Presentation Pack ..	..	4·00	□
		PHQ Cards (set of 4)	..	2·25	6·00 □ □
		Set of 4 Gutter Pairs	..	6·00	□

787 Dr. Edmond Halley as Comet

788 *Giotto* Spacecraft approaching Comet

789 "Twice in a Lifetime"

790 Comet orbiting Sun and Planets

Appearance of Halley's Comet

1986 (18 Feb.) *Phosphorised paper.*

1312	**787**	17p multicoloured	..	45	45 □ □
1313	**788**	22p multicoloured	..	90	90 □ □
1314	**789**	31p multicoloured	..	1·25	1·25 □ □
1315	**790**	34p multicoloured	..	1·25	1·25 □ □
		Set of 4 ..	.. ..	3·50	3·50 □ □
		First Day Cover ..	..		5·00 □
		Presentation Pack ..	..	4·50	□
		PHQ Cards (set of 4)	..	3·00	5·25 □ □
		Set of 4 Gutter Pairs	..	7·00	□

791 Queen Elizabeth II in 1928, 1942 and 1952

792 Queen Elizabeth II in 1958, 1973 and 1982

Nos. 1316/17 and 1318/19 were each printed together, *se-tenant*, in horizontal pairs throughout the sheets.

60th Birthday of Queen Elizabeth II

1986 (21 Apr.) *Phosphorised paper.*

1316	**791**	17p multicoloured	..	75	75 □ □
		a. Horiz pair.			
		Nos.1316/17	..	1·50	1·50 □ □
1317	**792**	17p multicoloured	..	75	75 □ □
1318	**791**	34p multicoloured	..	1·50	1·50 □ □
		a. Horiz pair.			
		Nos.1318/19	..	3·00	3·00 □ □
1319	**792**	34p multicoloured	..	1·50	1·50 □ □
		Set of 4 ..	.. ..	4·00	4·00 □ □
		First Day Cover ..	..		4·75 □
		Presentation Pack ..	..	5·00	□
		Souvenir Book ..	..	7·00	□
		PHQ Cards (set of 4)	..	2·75	5·50 □ □
		Set of 4 Gutter Pairs	..	8·00	□

793 Barn Owl

794 Pine Marten

795 Wild Cat

796 Natterjack Toad

Europa. Nature Conservation. Endangered Species

1986 (20 MAY) *Phosphorised paper. Perf* $14\frac{1}{2} \times 14$

1320	793	17p multicoloured	..	50	50	☐	☐
1321	794	22p multicoloured	..	90	90	☐	☐
1322	795	31p multicoloured	..	1·40	1·40	☐	☐
1323	796	34p multicoloured	..	1·40	1·40	☐	☐
		Set of 4		3·75	3·75	☐	☐
		First Day Cover			4·75	☐	
		Presentation Pack		5·00		☐	
		PHQ Cards (set of 4) ..		2·00	5·25	☐	☐
		Set of 4 Gutter Pairs		7·50		☐	

797 Peasants working in Fields

798 Freemen working at Town Trades

799 Knight and Retainers

800 Lord at Banquet

900th Anniversary of Domesday Book

1986 (17 JUNE) *Phosphorised paper*

1324	797	17p multicoloured	..	50	50	☐	☐
1325	798	22p multicoloured		90	90	☐	☐
1326	799	31p multicoloured	..	1·40	1·40	☐	☐
1327	800	34p multicoloured	..	1·40	1·40	☐	☐
		Set of 4		3·75	3·75	☐	☐
		First Day Cover			4·25		☐
		Presentation Pack		5·00			☐
		PHQ Cards (set of 4)		2·00	5·00	☐	☐
		Set of 4 Gutter Pairs		7·50			☐

801 Athletics

802 Rowing

803 Weightlifting

804 Rifle-Shooting

805 Hockey

Thirteenth Commonwealth Games, Edinburgh (Nos. 1328/31) and World Men's Hockey Cup, London (No. 1332)

1986 (15 JULY) *Phosphorised paper*.

1328	801	17p multicoloured	..	45	50	☐	☐
1329	802	22p multicoloured	..	90	60	☐	☐
1330	803	29p multicoloured	..	1·25	1·25	☐	☐
1331	804	31p multicoloured	..	1·25	1·25	☐	☐
1332	805	34p multicoloured	..	1·25	1·10	☐	☐
		Set of 5		4·50	4·00	☐	☐
		First Day Cover			5·75		☐
		Presentation Pack		5·25		☐	
		PHQ Cards (Set of 5)		2·40	5·75	☐	☐
		Set of 5 Gutter Pairs		9·00		☐	

No. 1332 also marked the centenary of the Hockey Association.

806 Prince Andrew and Miss Sarah Ferguson **807**

Royal Wedding

1986 (22 July) *One side band* (12p) *or phosphorised paper* (17p)

1333	**806**	12p multicoloured	..	60	60	☐	☐
1334	**807**	17p multicoloured	..	90	90	☐	☐
		Set of 2	.. .. ..	1·50	1·50	☐	☐
		First Day Cover	.. ..		2·50		☐
		Presentation Pack	.. ..	2·50		☐	
		PHQ Cards (set of 2)	..	1·00	3·00	☐	☐
		Set of 2 Gutter Pairs	.. ..	3·00		☐	

808 Stylised Cross on Ballot Paper

32nd Commonwealth Parliamentary Conference, London

1986 (19 Aug.) *Phosphorised paper. Perf* 14 × 14½

1335	**808**	34p multicoloured	..	1·50	1·50	☐	☐
		First Day Cover	.. .. ..		2·25		☐
		PHQ Card	.. ..	50	1·75	☐	☐
		Gutter Pair	.. .. ..	3·00		☐	

809 Lord Dowding and "Hurricane"

810 Lord Tedder and "Typhoon"

811 Lord Trenchard and "DH 9A"

812 Sir Arthur Harris and "Lancaster"

813 Lord Portal and "Mosquito"

History of the Royal Air Force

1986 (16th Sept.) *Phosphorised paper. Perf* 14½ × 14.

1336	**809**	17p multicoloured	..	45	40	☐	☐
1337	**810**	22p multicoloured	..	1·00	90	☐	☐
1338	**811**	29p multicoloured	..	1·25	1·10	☐	☐
1339	**812**	31p multicoloured	..	1·40	1·25	☐	☐
1340	**813**	34p multicoloured	..	1·50	1·25	☐	☐
		Set of 5	.. ..	5·00	4·50	☐	☐
		First Day Cover	.. ..		5·00		☐
		Presentation Pack	.. ..	6·00		☐	
		PHQ Cards (set of 5)	..	3·00	5·75	☐	☐
		Set of 5 Gutter Pairs	.. ..	10·00		☐	

Nos. 1336/40 were issued to celebrate the 50th anniversary of the first R.A.F. Commands.

814 The Glastonbury Thorn

815 The Tanad Valley Plygain

816 The Hebrides Tribute

817 The Dewsbury Church Knel

818 The Hereford Boy Bishop

Christmas. Folk Customs

986 *One phosphor band (12p, 13p) or phosphorised paper (others)*

341	**814**	12p mult. (2 Dec.)	..	75	75	☐	☐
342		13p mult. (18 Nov.)	..	40	40	☐	☐
343	**815**	18p mult. (18 Nov.)	..	55	55	☐	☐
344	**816**	22p mult. (18 Nov.)	..	75	75	☐	☐
345	**817**	31p mult. (18 Nov.)	..	1·00	1·00	☐	☐
346	**818**	34p mult. (18 Nov.)	..	1·00	1·00	☐	☐
		Set of 6		4·00	4·00	☐	☐
		First Day Covers (2)			5·25	☐	
		Presentation Pack (Nos. 1342/6)	5·00			☐	
		PHQ Cards (set of 5) (Nos. 1342/6)..		3·00	5·50	☐	☐
		Set of 6 Gutter Pairs		8·00		☐	

Collectors Pack 1986

986 (18 Nov.) *Comprises Nos. 1308/40, 1342/6*

	Collectors Pack	..	..	40·00	☐

Post Office Yearbook

1986 *Comprises Nos. 1308/40, 1342/6 in hardbound book with slip case.*

	Yearbook	..	..	95·00	☐

819 North American Blanket Flower

820 Globe Thistle

821 Echeveria

822 Autumn Crocus

Flower Photographs by Alfred Lammer

1987 (20 Jan.) *Phosphorised paper. Perf 14½ × 14*

1347	**819**	18p multicoloured	..	50	50	☐	☐
1348	**820**	22p multicoloured	..	80	80	☐	☐
1349	**821**	31p multicoloured	..	1·25	1·25	☐	☐
1350	**822**	34p multicoloured	..	1·40	1·40	☐	☐
		Set of 4		3·50	3·50	☐	☐
		First Day Cover			4·25	☐	
		Presentation Pack.. ..		4·50		☐	
		PHQ Cards (set of 4)		2·00	5·75	☐	☐
		Set of 4 Gutter Pairs		7·00		☐	

823 The Principia Mathematica

824 Motion of Bodies in Ellipses

825 Optick Treatise

826 The System of the World

300th Anniversary of The Principia Mathematica by Sir Isaac Newton

1987 (24 Mar.) *Phosphorised paper.*

1351	**823**	18p multicoloured	..	50	50	☐	☐
1352	**824**	22p multicoloured	..	80	80	☐	☐
1353	**825**	31p multicoloured	..	1·25	1·25	☐	☐
1354	**826**	34p multicoloured	..	1·40	1·40	☐	☐
		Set of 4		3·50	3·50	☐	☐
		First Day Cover			4·25	☐	
		Presentation Pack.. ..		4·50		☐	
		PHQ Cards (set of 4)		2·00	5·00	☐	☐
		Set of 4 Gutter Pairs		7·00		☐	

For full information on all future British issues, collectors should write to the British Post Office Philatelic Bureau, 20 Brandon Street, Edinburgh EH3 5TT

827 Willis Faber and Dumas Building, Ipswich

828 Pompidou Centre, Paris

829 Staatsgalerie, Stuttgart

830 European Investment Bank, Luxembourg

Europa. British Architects in Europe

1987 (12 May) *Phosphorised paper.*

1355	**827**	18p multicoloured	..	50	50	☐	☐
1356	**828**	22p multicoloured	..	80	80	☐	☐
1357	**829**	31p multicoloured	..	1·25	1·25	☐	☐
1358	**830**	34p multicoloured	..	1·40	1·40	☐	☐
		Set of 4	.. .. ..	3·50	3·50	☐	☐
		First Day Cover	.. ..		4·25	☐	
		Presentation Pack..	..	4·50		☐	
		PHQ Cards (set of 4)	..	2·00	5·00	☐	☐
		Set of 4 Gutter Pairs	.. ..	7·00		☐	

831 Brigade Members with Ashford Litter, 1887

832 Bandaging Blitz Victim, 1940

833 Volunteer with fainting Girl, 1965

834 Transport of Transplant Organ by Air Wing, 1987

Centenary of St. John Ambulance Brigade

1987 (16 June) *Phosphorised paper. Perf 14 × 14½*

1359	**831**	18p multicoloured	..	50	50	☐	☐
1360	**832**	22p multicoloured	..	80	80	☐	☐
1361	**833**	31p multicoloured	..	1·25	1·25	☐	☐
1362	**834**	34p multicoloured	..	1·40	1·40	☐	☐
		Set of 4	.. ..	3·50	3·50	☐	☐
		First Day Cover	..		4·25		☐
		Presentation Pack..	..	4·50		☐	
		PHQ Cards (set of 4)	..	2·00	5·00	☐	☐
		Set of 4 Gutter Pairs	..	7·00			

835 Arms of the Lord Lyon King of Arms

836 Scottish Heraldic Banner of Prince Charles

837 Arms of Royal Scottish Academy of Painting, Sculpture and Architecture

838 Arms of Royal Society of Edinburgh

300th Anniversary of Revival of Order of the Thistle

1987 (21 July) *Phosphorised paper. Perf 14½*

1363	**835**	18p multicoloured	..	50	50	☐	☐
1364	**836**	22p multicoloured	..	80	80	☐	☐
1365	**837**	31p multicoloured	..	1·25	1·25	☐	☐
1366	**838**	34p multicoloured	..	1·40	1·40	☐	☐
		Set of 4	.. .. ..	3·50	3·50	☐	☐
		First Day Cover	.. ..		4·25		☐
		Presentation Pack..	..	4·50		☐	
		PHQ Cards (set of 4)	..	2·00	5·00	☐	☐
		Set of 4 Gutter Pairs	..	7·00		☐	

839 Crystal Palace, 'Monarch of the Glen' (Landseer) and Grace Darling

840 Great Eastern, Beeton's Book of Household Management and Prince Albert

841 Albert Memorial, Ballot Box and Disraeli

842 Diamond Jubilee Emblem, Morse Key and Newspaper Placard for Relief of Mafeking

150th Anniversary of Queen Victoria's Accession

1987 (8 SEPT.) *Phosphorised paper.*

1367	**839**	18p multicoloured	..	50	50	☐	☐
1368	**840**	22p multicoloured	..	80	80	☐	☐
1369	**841**	31p multicoloured	..	1·25	1·25	☐	☐
1370	**842**	34p multicoloured	..	1·40	1·40	☐	☐
	Set of 4	.. .. ..	..	3·50	3·50	☐	☐
	First Day Cover	.. ..			4·25		☐
	Presentation Pack	..	..		4·50	☐	
	PHQ Cards (set of 4)	..	..	2·00	5·00	☐	☐
	Set of 4 Gutter Pairs	..	..	7·00		☐	

843 Pot by Bernard Leach

844 Pot by Elizabeth Fritsch

845 Pot by Lucie Rie

846 Pot by Hans Coper

Studio Pottery

1987 (13 OCT.) *Phosphorised paper. Perf* 14½ × 14

1371	**843**	18p multicoloured		50	50	☐	☐
1372	**844**	26p multicoloured		80	80	☐	☐
1373	**845**	31p multicoloured		1·25	1·25	☐	☐
1374	**846**	34p multicoloured		1·40	1·40	☐	☐
	Set of 4	.. ..		3·50	3·50	☐	☐
	First Day Cover	.. ..			4·25		☐
	Presentation Pack	.. ..		4·50		☐	
	PHQ Cards (set of 4)	.. ..		2·00	5·00	☐	☐
	Set of 4 Gutter Pairs	.. ..		7·00		☐	

Nos. 1371/4 also mark the birth centenary of Bernard Leach, the potter.

847 Decorating the Christmas tree

848 Waiting for Father Christmas

849 Sleeping Child and Father Christmas in Sleigh

850 Child reading

851 Child playing Flute and Snowman

Christmas

1987 (17 Nov.) *One phosphor band* (13p) *or phosphorised paper* (others)

1375	**847**	13p multicoloured	..	50	50	☐	☐
1376	**848**	18p multicoloured	..	60	60	☐	☐
1377	**849**	26p multicoloured	..	90	90	☐	☐
1378	**850**	31p multicoloured	..	1·10	1·10	☐	☐
1379	**851**	34p multicoloured	..	1·10	1·10	☐	☐
	Set of 5	.. ..	..	3·75	3·75	☐	☐
	First Day Cover	.. ..			4·25		☐
	Presentation Pack	..		4·50		☐	
	PHQ Cards (set of 5)	..		2·25	5·75	☐	☐
	Set of 5 Gutter Pairs	..		8·00		☐	

Collectors Pack 1987

1987 (17 Nov.) *Comprises Nos.* 1347/79
    Collectors Pack .. .. 35·00 ☐

Post Office Yearbook

1987 *Comprises Nos.* 1347/79 *in hardbound book with slip case*
    Yearbook .. .. .. 70·00 ☐

852 Bull-rout (Jonathan Couch)

853 Yellow Waterlily (Major Joshua Swatkin)

854 Bewick's Swan (Edward Lear)

855 *Morchella esculenta* (James Sowerby)

Bicentenary of Linnean Society. Archive Illustrations

1988 (19 Jan.) *Phosphorised paper*

1380	**852**	18p multicoloured	..	45	45 ☐ ☐
1381	**853**	26p multicoloured	..	85	85 ☐ ☐
1382	**854**	31p multicoloured	..	1·10	1·10 ☐ ☐
1383	**855**	34p multicoloured	..	1·25	1·25 ☐ ☐
		Set of 4		3·25	3·25 ☐ ☐
		First Day Cover			4·00 ☐
		Presentation Pack		4·50	☐
		PHQ Cards (set of 4) ..		2·00	5·00 ☐ ☐
		Set of 4 Gutter Pairs		6·50	☐

856 Revd William Morgan (Bible translator, 1588)

857 William Salesbury (New Testament translator, 1567)

858 Bishop Richard Davies (New Testament translator, 1567)

859 Bishop Richard Parry (editor of Revised Welsh Bible, 1620)

400th Anniversary of Welsh Bible

1988 (1 Mar.) *Phosphorised paper.* Perf $14\frac{1}{2} \times 14$

1384	**856**	18p multicoloured	..	45	45 ☐ ☐
1385	**857**	26p multicoloured	..	85	85 ☐ ☐
1386	**858**	31p multicoloured	..	1·10	1·10 ☐ ☐
1387	**859**	34p multicoloured	..	1·25	1·25 ☐ ☐
		Set of 4	..	.. 3·25	3·25 ☐ ☐
		First Day Cover			4·00 ☐
		Presentation Pack		4·50	☐
		PHQ Cards (set of 4) ..		2·00	5·00 ☐ ☐
		Set of 4 Gutter Pairs		6·50	☐

860 Gymnastics (Centenary of British Amateur Gymnastics Association)

861 Downhill Skiing (Ski Club of Great Britain)

862 Tennis (Centenary of Lawn Tennis Association)

863 Football (Centenary of Football League)

Sports Organizations

1988 (22 MAR.) *Phosphorised paper. Perf* 14½

1388	860	18p multicoloured	..	45	45	☐	☐
1389	861	26p multicoloured		85	85	☐	☐
1390	862	31p multicoloured		1·10	1·10	☐	☐
1391	863	34p multicoloured		1·25	1·25	☐	☐
		Set of 4	..	3·25	3·25	☐	☐
		First Day Cover			6·00	☐	
		Presentation Pack		4·50		☐	
		PHQ Cards (set of 4) ..		2·00	5·00	☐	☐
		Set of 4 Gutter Pairs ..		6·50		☐	

864 *Mallard* and Mailbags on Pick-up Arms

865 Loading Transatlantic Mail on Liner *Queen Elizabeth*

866 Glasgow Tram No. 1173 and Pillar Box

867 Imperial Airways Handley Page "HP 24" and Airmail Van

Europa. Transport and Mail Services in 1930's

1988 (10 MAY) *Phosphorised paper*

1392	864	18p multicoloured	..	50	50	☐	☐
1393	865	26p multicoloured	..	80	80	☐	☐
1394	866	31p multicoloured	..	1·10	1·10	☐	☐
1395	867	34p multicoloured	..	1·25	1·25	☐	☐
		Set of 4	..	3·25	3·25	☐	☐
		First Day Cover			4·25	☐	
		Presentation Pack		4·50		☐	
		PHQ Cards (set of 4) ..		2·00	5·00	☐	☐
		Set of 4 Gutter Pairs ..		6·50		☐	

868 Early Settler and Sailing Clipper

869 Queen Elizabeth II with British and Australian Parliament Buildings

870 W. G. Grace (cricketer) and Tennis Racquet

871 Shakespeare, John Lennon (entertainer) and Sydney Landmarks

Nos. 1396/7 and 1398/9 were each printed together, *se-tenant*, in horizontal pairs throughout the sheets, each pair showing a background design of the Australian flag.

Bicentenary of Australian Settlement

1988 (21 JUNE) *Phosphorised paper. Perf* 14½

1396	868	18p multicoloured	..	60	60	☐	☐
		a. Horiz pair.					
		Nos. 1396/7 ..		1·25	1·25	☐	☐
1397	869	18p multicoloured	..	60	60	☐	☐
1398	870	34p multicoloured	..	1·10	1·10	☐	☐
		a. Horiz pair.					
		Nos. 1398/9 ..		2·40	2·40	☐	☐
1399	871	34p multicoloured	..	1·10	1·10	☐	☐
		Set of 4	..	3·25	3·25	☐	☐
		First Day Cover			4·25	☐	
		Presentation Pack		4·50		☐	
		Souvenir Book ..		6·00		☐	
		PHQ Cards (set of 4) ..		2·00	5·00	☐	☐
		Set of 4 Gutter Pairs ..		6·50		☐	

Stamps in similar designs were also issued by Australia.

872 Spanish Galeasse off The Lizard

873 English Fleet leaving Plymouth

874 Engagement off Isle of Wight

875 Attack of English Fire-ships, Calais

876 Armada in Storm,
North Sea

Nos. 1400/4 were printed together, *se-tenant*, in horizontal strips of 5 throughout the sheet, forming a composite design.

400th Anniversary of Spanish Armada

1988 (19 JULY) *Phosphorised paper*

1400	**872**	18p multicoloured	..	65	65	☐ ☐
		a. *Horiz strip of* 5.				
		Nos. 1400/4 ..	..	2·75	2·75	☐ ☐
1401	**873**	18p multicoloured	..	65	65	☐ ☐
1402	**874**	18p multicoloured	..	65	65	☐ ☐
1403	**875**	18p multicoloured	..	65	65	☐ ☐
1404	**876**	18p multicoloured	..	65	65	☐ ☐
		Set of 5	..	2·75	2·75	☐ ☐
		First Day Cover ..	..		3·75	☐
		Presentation Pack ..	..	4·00		☐
		PHQ Cards (set of 5)	..	2·00	5·50	☐ ☐
		Gutter strip of 10	..	5·50		☐

877 "The Owl and the
Pussy-cat"

878 "Edward Lear as a Bird"
(self-portrait)

879 "Cat" (from alphabet
book)

880 "There was a Young Lady
whose Bonnet . . ."
(limerick)

Death Centenary of Edward Lear (artist and author)

1988 (6–27 SEPT.) *Phosphorised paper*

1405	**877**	19p black, pale cream and carmine	50	50	☐ ☐
1406	**878**	27p black, pale cream and yellow	80	80	☐ ☐
1407	**879**	32p black, pale cream and emerald	1·10	1·10	☐ ☐
1408	**880**	35p black, pale cream and blue	1·25	1·25	☐ ☐
		Set of 4	3·25	3·25	☐ ☐
		First Day Cover ..		4·00	☐
		Presentation Pack ..	4·50		☐
		PHQ Cards (set of 4) ..	2·00	5·00	☐ ☐
		Set of 4 Gutter Pairs ..	6·50		☐
MS1409		122×90 mm. Nos. 1405/8	12·00	7·50	☐ ☐
		First Day Cover (27 Sept.) ..		8·00	☐

No. **MS**1409 was sold at £1·35, the premium being used for the "Stamp World London 90" International Stamp Exhibition.

CARRICKFERGUS CASTLE

881 Carrickfergus Castle

CAERNARFON CASTLE

882 Caernarvon Castle

EDINBURGH CASTLE

883 Edinburgh Castle

WINDSOR CASTLE

884 Windsor Castle

1988 (18 OCT.) *Ordinary paper*

1410	**881**	£1 deep green	..	..	2·25	50	☐ ☐
1411	**882**	£1·50 maroon	..	..	3·25	1·00	☐ ☐
1412	**883**	£2 indigo	..	..	4·50	1·50	☐ ☐
1413	**884**	£5 deep brown	..	..	11·00	3·00	☐ ☐
		Set of 4	..	19·00	5·50	☐ ☐
		First Day Cover ..	..		45·00	☐
		Presentation Pack ..	..	22·00		☐
		Set of 4 Gutter Pairs	..	38·00		☐

For similar designs, but with silhouette Queen's head see Nos. 1611/14.

885 Journey to Bethlehem

886 Shepherds and Star

887 Three Wise Men

888 Nativity

889 The Annunciation

890 Puffin

891 Avocet

892 Oystercatcher

893 Gannet

Christmas

1988 (15 Nov.) *One phosphor band* (14p) *or phosphorised paper* (*others*)

1414	**885**	14p multicoloured	..	35	35	☐	☐
1415	**886**	19p multicoloured	..	50	50	☐	☐
1416	**887**	27p multicoloured	..	80	80	☐	☐
1417	**888**	32p multicoloured	..	1·10	1·10	☐	☐
1418	**889**	35p multicoloured	..	1·25	1·25	☐	☐
		Set of 5	..	3·50	3·50	☐	☐
		First Day Cover	..		4·25	☐	
		Presentation Pack ..	..	4·25		☐	
		PHQ Cards (set of 5)	..	2·00	5·25	☐	☐
		Set of 5 Gutter Pairs	..	7·00		☐	

Collectors Pack 1988

1988 (15 Nov.) *Comprises Nos.* 1380/1408, 1414/18
	Collectors Pack	.. ..	30·00	☐

Post Office Yearbook

1988 *Comprises Nos.* 1380/1404. **MS**1409, 1414/18 *in hardbound book with slip case*
Yearbook	.. .. ..	50·00	☐

Centenary of Royal Society for the Protection of Birds

1989 (17 Jan.) *Phosphorised paper*

1419	**890**	19p multicoloured	..	50	50	☐	☐
1420	**891**	27p multicoloured	..	1·10	1·10	☐	☐
1421	**892**	32p multicoloured	..	1·25	1·25	☐	☐
1422	**893**	35p multicoloured	..	1·10	1·10	☐	☐
		Set of 4	..	3·50	3·50	☐	☐
		First Day Cover	..		4·50	☐	
		Presentation Pack ..	..	4·50		☐	
		PHQ Cards (set of 4)	..	2·00	5·00	☐	☐
		Set of 4 Gutter Pairs	..	7·00		☐	

894 Rose

895 Cupid

896 Yachts

897 Fruit

898 Teddy Bear

Nos. 1423/7 were printed together, *se-tenant*, in horizontal strips of five, two such strips forming the booklet pane.

Greetings Booklet Stamps

1989 (31 Jan.) *Phosphorised paper*

1423	**894**	19p multicoloured	..	3·00	2·25 ☐ ☐
		a. *Booklet pane.*			
		Nos. 1423/7 × 2	..	28·00	☐
1424	**895**	19p multicoloured	..	3·00	2·25 ☐ ☐
1425	**896**	19p multicoloured	..	3·00	2·25 ☐ ☐
1426	**897**	19p multicoloured	..	3·00	2·25 ☐ ☐
1427	**898**	19p multicoloured	..	3·00	2·25 ☐ ☐
		Set of 5	..	14·00	10·00 ☐ ☐
		First Day Cover	..		10·00 ☐

899 Fruit and Vegetables

900 Meat Products

901 Dairy Produce

902 Cereal Products

Food and Farming Year

1989 (7 Mar.) *Phosphorised paper. Perf* 14 × 14½

1428	**899**	19p multicoloured	..	50	50 ☐ ☐
1429	**900**	27p multicoloured	..	80	80 ☐ ☐
1430	**901**	32p multicoloured	..	1·10	1·10 ☐ ☐
1431	**902**	35p multicoloured	..	1·25	1·25 ☐ ☐
		Set of 4	..	3·25	3·25 ☐ ☐
		First Day Cover	..		4·25 ☐
		Presentation Pack ..	..	4·50	☐
		PHQ Cards (*set of* 4)	..	2·00	5·00 ☐ ☐
		Set of 4 *Gutter Pairs*	..	6·50	☐

903 Mortar Board (150th Anniv of Public Education in England)

904 Cross on Ballot Paper (3rd Direct Elections to European Parliament)

905 Posthorn (26th Postal, Telegraph and Telephone International Congress Brighton)

906 Globe (Inter-Parliamentary Union Centenary Conference, London)

Nos. 1432/3 and 1434/5 were each printed together, *se-tenant*, in horizontal pairs throughout the sheets.

Anniversaries

1989 (11 Apr.) *Phosphorised paper. Perf* 14 × 14½

1432	**903**	19p multicoloured	..	55	55 ☐ ☐
		a. *Horiz pair.*			
		Nos. 1432/3	..	1·10	1·10 ☐ ☐
1433	**904**	19p multicoloured	..	55	55 ☐ ☐
1434	**905**	35p multicoloured	..	1·10	1·10 ☐ ☐
		a. *Horiz pair.*			
		Nos. 1434/5	..	2·25	2·25 ☐ ☐
1435	**906**	35p multicoloured	..	1·10	1·10 ☐ ☐
		Set of 4	..	3·00	3·00 ☐ ☐
		First Day Cover	..		4·25 ☐
		Presentation Pack ..	..	4·50	☐
		PHQ Cards (*set of* 4)	..	2·00	5·00 ☐ ☐
		Set of 2 *Gutter Pairs*	..	3·00	☐

907 Toy Train and Airplane

908 Building Bricks

909 Dice and Board Games

910 Toy Robot, Boat and Doll's House

Europa. Games and Toys

1989 (16 MAY) *Phosphorised paper*

1436	**907**	19p multicoloured	..	50	50	☐	☐
1437	**908**	27p multicoloured	..	80	80	☐	☐
1438	**909**	32p multicoloured	..	1·10	1·10	☐	☐
1439	**910**	35p multicoloured	..	1·25	1·25	☐	☐
		Set of 4	..	3·25	3·25	☐	☐
		First Day Cover ..	.. ..		4·25	☐	
		Presentation Pack ..	.. ..	4·50			
		PHQ Cards (set of 4)	.. ..	2·00	5·00	☐	☐
		Set of 4 Gutter Pairs	..	6·50		☐	

911 Ironbridge, Shropshire

912 Tin Mine, St. Agnes Head, Cornwall

913 Cotton Mills, New Lanark, Strathclyde

914 Pontcysyllte Aqueduct, Clwyd

915

Industrial Archaeology

1989 (4–25 JULY) *Phosphorised paper*

1440	**911**	19p multicoloured	..	50	50	☐	☐
1441	**912**	27p multicoloured	..	80	80	☐	☐
1442	**913**	32p multicoloured	..	1·00	1·00	☐	☐
1443	**914**	35p multicoloured	..	1·10	1·10	☐	☐
		Set of 4	..	3·00	3·00	☐	☐
		First Day Cover ..	.. ..		4·25	☐	
		Presentation Pack ..	.. ..	4·50			
		PHQ Cards (set of 4)	.. ..	2·00	5·00	☐	☐
		Set of 4 Gutter Pairs	..	6·50		☐	

MS1444 122 × 90 mm. **915** As Nos.
1440/3 but designs horizontal .. 8·00 6·00 ☐ ☐
First Day Cover (25 July) 6·00

No.**MS**1444 was sold at £1.40, the premium being used for the "Stamp World London 90" International Stamp Exhibition.

916

917

Booklet Stamps

1989 (22 AUG.)–**92**

(a) Printed in photogravure by Harrison and Sons. Perf 15 × 14

1445	**916**	(2nd) bright blue (1 centre band)	45	45	☐	☐
1446		(2nd) bright blue (1 side band) (20.3.90)	4·00	4·00	☐	☐
1447	**917**	(1st) black (phosphorised paper)	1·00	50	☐	☐
1448		(1st) brownish black (2 bands) (20.3.90) ..	4·00	4·00	☐	☐

(b) Printed in lithography by Walsall. Perf 14

1449	**916**	(2nd) bright blue (1 centre band) ..	30	35	☐	☐
1450	**917**	(1st) black (2 bands) ..	1·75	1·75	☐	☐

(c) Printed in lithography by Questa. Perf 15 × 14

1451 **916**	(2nd) bright blue (1 centre band) (19.9.89)	30	35	☐	☐
1451*a*	(2nd) bright blue (1 side band) (25.2.92) ..	2·10	2·10	☐	☐
1452 **917**	(1st) black (phosphorised paper) (19.9.89) ..	1·10	1·10	☐	☐
	First Day Cover (Nos. 1445, 1447)		3·50	☐	

For similar stamps showing changed colours see Nos. 1511/16.

918 Snowflake (× 10)

919 *Calliphora erythrocephala* (fly) (× 5)

920 Blood Cells (× 500)

921 Microchip (× 600)

150th Anniversary of Royal Microscopical Society

1989 (5 Sept.) *Phosphorised paper. Perf* 14½ × 14

1453 **918**	19p multicoloured	..	50	50	☐	☐
1454 **919**	27p multicoloured	..	85	85	☐	☐
1455 **920**	32p multicoloured	..	1·00	1·00	☐	☐
1456 **921**	35p multicoloured	..	1·00	1·00	☐	☐
	Set of 4	..	3·00	3·00	☐	☐
	First Day Cover	..		5·00	☐	
	Presentation Pack ..	..	4·00		☐	
	PHQ Cards (set of 4)	..	2·00	5·00	☐	☐
	Set of 4 Gutter Pairs	..	6·00		☐	

Minimum Price. The minimum price quoted is 10p. This represents a handling charge rather than a basis for valuing common stamps. Where the actual value of a stamp is less than 10p this may be apparent when set prices are shown, particularly for sets including a number of 10p stamps. It therefore follows that in valuing common stamps the 10p catalogue price should not be reckoned automatically since it covers a variation in real scarcity.

922 Royal Mail Coach

923 Escort of Blues and Royals

924 Lord Mayor's Coach

925 Coach Team passing St Paul's

926 Blues and Royals Drum Horse

Nos. 1457/61 were printed together, *se-tenant*, in horizontal strips of 5 throughout the sheet, forming a composite design.

Lord Mayor's Show, London

1989 (17 Oct.) *Phosphorised paper*

1457 **922**	20p multicoloured	..	60	60	☐	☐
	a. Horiz strip of 5. Nos. 1457/61 ..	2·75	2·75	☐	☐
1458 **923**	20p multicoloured	..	60	60	☐	☐
1459 **924**	20p multicoloured	..	60	60	☐	☐
1460 **925**	20p multicoloured	..	60	60	☐	☐
1461 **926**	20p multicoloured	..	60	60	☐	☐
	Set of 5	..	2·75	2·75	☐	☐
	First Day Cover ..	..		3·75	☐	
	Presentation Pack ..	..	4·25		☐	
	PHQ Cards (set of 5)	..	2·00	4·50	☐	☐
	Gutter Strip of 10	..	5·50		☐	

Nos. 1457/61 commemorate the 800th anniversary of the installation of the first Lord Mayor of London.

927 14th-century Peasants from Stained-glass Window

928 Arches and Roundels, West Front

929 Octagon Tower

930 Arcade from West Transept

931 Triple Arch from West Front

Christmas. 800th Anniversary of Ely Cathedral

1989 (14 Nov.) *One phosphor band (Nos. 1462/3) or phosphorised paper (others)*

1462	**927**	15p gold, silver and blue	35	35	☐	☐
1463	**928**	15p + 1p gold, silver and blue	50	50	☐	☐
1464	**929**	20p + 1p gold, silver and rosine	60	60	☐	☐
1465	**930**	34p + 1p gold, silver and emerald	1·10	1·10	☐	☐
1466	**931**	37p + 1p gold, silver and yellow-olive	1·10	1·10	☐	☐
		Set of 5	3·25	3·25	☐	☐
		First Day Cover		4·00		☐
		Presentation Pack	4·50		☐	
		PHQ Cards (set of 5)	2·00	5·00	☐	☐
		Set of 5 Gutter Pairs	6·50		☐	

Collectors Pack 1989

1989 (14 Nov.) *Comprises Nos. 1419/22, 1428/43 and 1453/66*

Collectors Pack	.. ..	28·00	☐

Post Office Yearbook

1989 (14 Nov) *Comprises Nos. 1419/22, 1428/44 and 1453/66 in hardback book with slip case.*

Yearbook	.. ..	50·00	☐

932 Queen Victoria and Queen Elizabeth II

150th Anniversary of the Penny Black

1990 (10 Jan.–12 June)

(a) Printed in photogravure by Harrison and Sons. Perf 15 × 14

1467	**932**	15p bright blue (1 centre band)	55	55	☐	☐
1468		15p bright blue (1 side band) (30 Jan) ..	2·00	2·00	☐	☐
1469		20p brownish black and cream (phosphorised paper)	75	75	☐	☐
1470		20p brnish blk & cream (2 bands) (30 Jan)	1·10	1·10	☐	☐
1471		29p deep mauve (phosphorised paper) ..	1·00	1·00	☐	☐
1472		29p deep mauve (2 bands) (20 Mar) ..	4·50	4·50	☐	☐
1473		34p deep bluish grey (phosphorised paper)	1·25	1·25	☐	☐
1474		37p rosine (phosphorised paper)	1·40	1·40	☐	☐
		Set of 5 (Nos. 1467, 1469, 1471, 1473/4)	4·50	4·50	☐	☐
		First Day Cover (Nos. 1467, 1469, 1471, 1473/4) ..		6·00		☐
		Presentation Pack (Nos. 1467, 1469, 1471, 1473/4)	5·75		☐	

(b) Litho Walsall. Perf 14 (30 Jan)

1475	**932**	15p bright blue (1 centre band)	75	75	☐	☐
1476		20p brnish blk & cream (phosphorised paper)	1·50	1·50	☐	☐

(c) Litho Questa. Perf 15 × 14 (17 Apr)

1477	**932**	15p bright blue (1 centre band)	1·00	1·00	☐	☐
1478		20p brnish black (phosphorised paper) ..	1·50	1·25	☐	☐

No. 1468 exists with the phosphor band at the left or right of the stamp.

933 Kitten

934 Rabbit

935 Duckling

936 Puppy

150th Anniversary of Royal Society for Prevention of Cruelty to Animals

1990 (23 JAN.) *Phosphorised paper. Perf* 14 × 14½.

1479	**933**	20p multicoloured	..	50	50	☐	☐
1480	**934**	29p multicoloured	..	80	80	☐	☐
1481	**935**	34p multicoloured	..	1·00	1·00	☐	☐
1482	**936**	37p multicoloured	..	1·10	1·10	☐	☐
		Set of 4	..	3·00	3·00	☐	
		First Day Cover			5·25	☐	
		Presentation Pack		5·00		☐	
		PHQ Cards (set of 4)		2·00	4·75	☐ ☐	
		Set of 4 Gutter Pairs		6·00		☐	

937 Teddy Bear

938 Dennis the Menace

939 Punch

940 Cheshire Cat

941 The Man in the Moon

942 The Laughing Policeman

943 Clown

944 Mona Lisa

945 Queen of Hearts

946 Stan Laurel (comedian)

T **937**/46 were printed together, *se-tenant*, in booklet panes of 10.

Greetings Booklet Stamps. "Smiles"

1990 (6 FEB.) *Two phosphor bands*

1483	**937**	20p multicoloured	..	75	75	☐	☐
		a. Booklet pane.					
		Nos. 1483/92	..	12·00		☐	
1484	**938**	20p multicoloured	..	75	75	☐	☐
1485	**939**	20p multicoloured	..	75	75	☐	☐
1486	**940**	20p multicoloured	..	75	75	☐	☐
1487	**941**	20p multicoloured	..	75	75	☐	☐
1488	**942**	20p multicoloured	..	75	75	☐	☐
1489	**943**	20p multicoloured	..	75	75	☐	☐
1490	**944**	20p multicoloured	..	75	75	☐	☐
1491	**945**	20p multicoloured	..	75	75	☐	☐
1492	**946**	20p gold and grey-black	..	75	75	☐	☐
		Set of 10		12·00	7·50	☐	☐
		First Day Cover			12·00		☐

For those designs with the face value expressed as "1st
see Nos. 1550/9.

947 Alexandra Palace ("Stamp World London 90" Exhibition)

948 Glasgow School of Art

949 British Philatelic Bureau, Edinburgh

950 Templeton Carpet Factory, Glasgow

Europa (Nos. 1493 and 1495) and "Glasgow 1990 European City of Culture" (Nos. 1494 and 1496)

1990 (6 Mar.) *Phosphorised paper*

1493	**947**	20p multicoloured	..	50	50	□	□
1494	**948**	20p multicoloured	..	80	80	□	□
1495	**949**	29p multicoloured	..	1·00	1·00	□	□
1496	**950**	37p multicoloured	..	1·10	1·10	□	□
		Set of 4		3·00	3·00	□	□
		First Day Cover			4·25		□
		Presentation Pack		4·00		□	
		PHQ Cards (set of 4) ..		2·00	5·25	□	□
		Set of 4 Gutter Pairs		6·50		□	

951 Export Achievement Award

952 Technological Achievement Award

Nos. 1497/8 and 1499/500 were each printed together, *se-tenant,* in horizontal pairs throughout the sheets.

25th Anniversary of Queen's Awards for Export and Technology

1990 (10 Apr.) *Phosphorised paper. Perf* 14 × 14½.

1497	**951**	20p multicoloured	..	55	55	□	□
		a. Horiz pair.					
		Nos. 1497/8 ..	..	1·10	1·10	□	□
1498	**952**	20p multicoloured	..	55	55	□	□
1499	**951**	37p multicoloured	..	1·10	1·10	□	□
		a. Horiz pair.					
		Nos. 1499/500	..	2·25	2·25	□	□
1500	**952**	37p multicoloured	..	1·10	1·10	□	□
		Set of 4		3·00	3·00	□	□
		First Day Cover			4·50		□
		Presentation Pack ..		4·00		□	
		PHQ Cards (set of 4)		2·00	5·25	□	□
		Set of 2 Gutter Pairs		6·00		□	

953

"Stamp World 90" International Stamp Exhibition, London

1990 (3 May.) *Sheet* 122 × 90 *mm. Phosphorised paper*

MS1501	**953**	20p. brownish black					
		and cream	.. .. ..	3·25	3·25	□	□
		First Day Cover			5·50		□
		Souvenir Book (Nos. 1467,					
		1469, 1471, 1473/4 *and*					
		MS1501)		12·00		□	

No. **MS**1501 was sold at £1, the premium being used for the exhibition.

954 Cycad and Sir Joseph Banks Building

955 Stone Pine and Princess of Wales Conservatory

956 Willow Tree and Palm House

957 Cedar Tree and Pagoda

150th Anniversary of Kew Gardens

1990 (5 June) *Phosphorised paper*

1502	**954**	20p multicoloured	..	50	50	□	□
1503	**955**	29p multicoloured	..	80	80	□	□

1504	**956**	34p multicoloured	..	1·10	1·25	☐	☐
1505	**957**	37p multicoloured	..	1·25	1·40	☐	☐
		Set of 4	.. .. ..	3·25	3·50	☐	☐
		First Day Cover	.. ..		4·50	☐	
		Presentation Pack	..	4·00		☐	
		PHQ Cards (set of 4)	..	2·00	4·75	☐	☐
		Set of 4 Gutter Pairs	.. ..	6·50		☐	

958 Thomas Hardy and Clyffe Clump, Dorset

150th Birth Anniversary of Thomas Hardy (author)

1990 (10 JULY) *Phosphorised paper*

1506	**958**	20p multicoloured	..	60	70	☐	☐
		First Day Cover	.. ..		2·00	☐	
		Presentation Pack	.. ..	1·75		☐	
		PHQ Card	.. ..	50	2·00	☐	☐
		Gutter Pair	.. ..	1·25		☐	

959 Queen Elizabeth the Queen Mother

960 Queen Elizabeth

961 Elizabeth, Duchess of York

962 Lady Elizabeth Bowes-Lyon

90th Birthday of Queen Elizabeth the Queen Mother

1990 (2 AUG.) *Phosphorised paper*

1507	**959**	20p multicoloured	..	50	50	☐	☐
1508	**960**	29p silver, indigo and grey-blue	.. ..	80	80	☐	☐

1509	**961**	34p multicoloured	..	1·10	1·25	☐	☐
1510	**962**	37p silver, sepia and stone	.. .. ..	1·25	1·40	☐	☐
		Set of 4	.. .. ..	3·25	3·50	☐	☐
		First Day Cover	.. ..		5·50	☐	
		Presentation Pack	..	4·50		☐	
		PHQ Cards (set of 4)	..	2·00	5·25	☐	☐
		Set of 4 Gutter Pairs	.. ..	6·50		☐	

Booklet Stamps

1990 (7 AUG.)-**92** *As Types* **916/17**, *but colours changed*

(a) Photo Harrison, Perf 15 × 14

1511	**916**	(2nd) dp blue (1 centre band)	.. ..	45	45	☐	☐
1512	**917**	(1st) brt orge-red (phosphorised paper)	..	30	35	☐	☐

(a) Litho Questa. Perf 15 × 14

1513	**916**	(2nd) dp blue (1 centre band)	.. ..	45	45	☐	☐
1514	**917**	(1st) brt orge-red (phosphorised paper)	..	45	45	☐	☐
1514a		(1st) brt orange-red (2 bands) (25.2.92)	..	2·25	2·25	☐	☐

(c) Litho Walsall. Perf 14

1515	**916**	(2nd) dp blue (1 centre band)	.. ..	50	50	☐	☐
1516	**917**	(1st) brt orge-red (phosphorised paper)	..	30	35	☐	☐
		First Day Cover (Nos. 1515/16)			3·00	☐	

963 Victoria Cross

964 George Cross

965 Distinguished Service Cross and Distinguished Service Medal

966 Military Cross and Military Medal

967 Distinguished Flying Cross and Distinguished Flying Medal

Gallantry Awards

1990 (11 SEPT.) *Phosphorised paper*

1517	**963**	20p multicoloured	..	65	65	☐	☐
1518	**964**	20p multicoloured		65	65	☐	☐
1519	**965**	20p multicoloured		65	65	☐	☐
1520	**966**	20p multicoloured		65	65	☐	☐
1521	**967**	20p multicoloured	..	65	65	☐	☐
		Set of 5	..	3·00	3·00	☐	☐
		First Day Cover			4·50		☐
		Presentation Pack ..		4·00		☐	
		PHQ Cards (set of 5) ..	..	2·00	4·75	☐	☐
		Set of 5 Gutter Pairs ..	..	6·00		☐	

968 Armagh Observatory, Jodrell Bank Radio Telescope and La Palma Telescope

969 Newton's Moon and Tides Diagram with Early Telescopes

970 Greenwich Old Observatory and Early Astronomical Equipment

971 Stonehenge, Gyroscope and Navigating by Stars

Astronomy

1990 (16 OCT.) *Phosphorised paper. Perf* 14 × 14½

1522	**968**	22p multicoloured	..	50	40	☐	☐
1523	**969**	26p multicoloured		80	90	☐	☐
1524	**970**	31p multicoloured	..	1·00	1·00	☐	☐
1525	**971**	37p multicoloured	..	1·10	1·10	☐	☐
		Set of 4	..	3·00	3·00	☐	☐
		First Day Cover			4·00		☐
		Presentation Pack ..		4·00		☐	
		PHQ Cards (set of 4) ..	..	2·00	4·75	☐	☐
		Set of 4 Gutter Pairs ..		6·00		☐	

Nos. 1522/5 commemorate the centenary of the British Astronomical Association and the bicentenary of the Armagh Observatory.

972 Building a Snowman

973 Fetching the Christmas Tree

974 Carol Singing

975 Tobogganing

976 Ice-skating

Christmas

1990 (13 Nov.) *One phosphor band* (17p) *or phosphorised paper (others)*

1526	**972**	17p multicoloured	..	45	35	☐	☐
1527	**973**	22p multicoloured	..	55	65	☐	☐
1528	**974**	26p multicoloured	..	80	80	☐	☐
1529	**975**	31p multicoloured	..	1·00	1·00	☐	☐
1530	**976**	37p multicoloured	..	1·10	1·10	☐	☐
		Set of 5	..	3·50	3·50	☐	☐
		First Day Cover			4·25		☐
		Presentation Pack ..		4·25		☐	
		PHQ Cards (set of 5) ..	..	2·50	5·00	☐	☐
		Set of 5 Gutter Pairs ..	..	7·00		☐	

Collectors Pack 1990

1990 (13 Nov.) *Comprises Nos.* 1479/82, 1493/1510 *and* 1517/30

	Collectors Pack	28·00	☐

Post Office Yearbook

1990 *Comprises Nos.* 1479/82, 1493/500, 1502/10 *and* 1517/30 *in hardback book with slip case.*

	Yearbook	48·00	☐

977 "King Charles Spaniel"

978 "A Pointer"

979 "Two Hounds in a Landscape"

980 "A Rough Dog"

981 "Fino and Tiny"

Dogs. Paintings by George Stubbs

1991 (8 Jan.) *Phosphorised paper. Perf 14 × 14½*

1531	**977**	22p multicoloured	..	75	75	☐	☐
1532	**978**	26p multicoloured	..	80	80	☐	☐
1533	**979**	31p multicoloured	..	85	85	☐	☐
1534	**980**	33p multicoloured	..	95	95	☐	☐
1535	**981**	37p multicoloured	..	1·10	1·10	☐	☐
		Set of 5	.. .. ..	4·00	4·00	☐	☐
		First Day Cover	.. ..		5·00		☐
		Presentation Pack	.. ..	5·00		☐	
		PHQ Cards (set of 5)	.. ..	2·00	4·50	☐	☐
		Set of 5 Gutter Pairs	.. ..	7·00		☐	

983 Shooting Star and Rainbow

982 Thrush's Nest

984 Magpies and Charm Bracelet

985 Black Cat

986 Kingfisher with Key

987 Duck and Frog

988 Four-leaf Clover in Boot and Match Box

989 Pot of Gold at End of Rainbow

990 Heart-shaped Butterflies

991 Wishing Well and Sixpence

T **982/91** were printed together, *se-tenant*, in booklet panes of 10, the backgrounds of the stamps forming a composite design.

Greetings Booklet Stamps. "Good Luck"

1991 (5 Feb.) *Two phosphor bands.*

1536	**982**	(1st) multicoloured	..	60	60	☐	☐
		a. Booklet pane. Nos. 1536/45 plus 12 half stamp-size labels	..	7·00		☐	
1537	**983**	(1st) multicoloured	..	60	60	☐	☐
1538	**984**	(1st) multicoloured	..	60	60	☐	☐
1539	**985**	(1st) multicoloured	..	60	60	☐	☐
1540	**986**	(1st) multicoloured	..	60	60	☐	☐
1541	**987**	(1st) multicoloured	..	60	60	☐	☐
1542	**988**	(1st) multicoloured	..	60	60	☐	☐
1543	**989**	(1st) multicoloured	..	60	60	☐	☐
1544	**990**	(1st) multicoloured	..	60	60	☐	☐
1545	**991**	(1st) multicoloured	..	60	60	☐	☐
		Set of 10	.. .. ..	7·00	5·50	☐	☐
		First Day Cover	.. ..		8·50		☐

992 Michael Faraday
(inventor of
electric motor)
(Birth Bicentenary)

993 Charles Babbage
(computer
science pioneer)
(Birth Bicentenary)

994 Radar Sweep of
East Anglia (50th
Anniv of Discovery
by Sir Robert
Watson-Watt)

995 Gloster E28/39
Aircraft over East
Anglia (50th
Anniv of First
Flight of Sir Frank
Whittle's Jet Engine)

Scientific Achievements

1991 (5 Mar.) *Phosphorised paper*

1546	**992**	22p multicoloured	..	60	60	☐	☐
1547	**993**	22p multicoloured	..	60	60	☐	☐
1548	**994**	31p multicoloured	..	85	85	☐	☐
1549	**995**	37p multicoloured	..	95	95	☐	☐
	Set of 4	..	..	2·75	2·75	☐	☐
	First Day Cover	..	..		4·00		☐
	Presentation Pack	..	..	3·50		☐	
	PHQ Cards (set of 4)	..	2·00	4·25	☐	☐	
	Set of 4 Gutter Pairs	..	..	5·50		☐	

996 Teddy Bear

Nos. 1550/9 were printed together, *se-tenant*, in booklet panes of 10.

Greetings Booklet Stamps. "Smiles"

1991 (26 Mar.) *As Nos.* 1483/92, *but inscribed* "1st" *as T* **996**. *Two phosphor bands.*

1550	**996**	(1st) multicoloured ..	35	40	☐	☐
		a. Booklet pane. Nos. 1550/9 plus 12 half stamp-size labels ..	3·25		☐	
1551	**938**	(1st) multicoloured	35	40	☐	☐
1552	**939**	(1st) multicoloured	35	40	☐	☐
1553	**940**	(1st) multicoloured	35	40	☐	☐
1554	**941**	(1st) multicoloured	35	40	☐	☐
1555	**942**	(1st) multicoloured	35	40	☐	☐
1556	**943**	(1st) multicoloured	35	40	☐	☐
1557	**944**	(1st) multicoloured	35	40	☐	☐
1558	**945**	(1st) multicoloured	35	40	☐	☐
1559	**946**	(1st) multicoloured	35	40	☐	☐
	Set of 10	.. .. ..	3·25	3·50	☐	☐
	First Day Cover	.. ..		7·50		☐

997 Man looking at Space

998

999 Space looking at Man

1000

Nos. 1560/1 and 1562/3 were each printed together, *se-tenant*, in horizontal pairs throughout the sheets, each pair forming a composite design.

Europa. Europe in Space

1991 (23 Apr.) *Phosphorised paper.*

1560	**997**	22p multicoloured ..	55	55	☐	☐
		a. Horiz pair. Nos. 1560/1	1·10	1·10	☐	☐
1561	**998**	22p multicoloured	55	55	☐	☐
1562	**999**	37p multicoloured ..	1·00	1·00	☐	☐
		a. Horiz pair. Nos. 1562/3	2·00	2·00	☐	☐
1563	**1000**	37p multicoloured ..	1·00	1·00	☐	☐
	Set of 4	.. .. ..	2·75	2·75	☐	☐
	First Day Cover	.. ..		4·00		☐
	Presentation Pack	.. ..	4·00		☐	
	PHQ Cards (set of 4)	.. ..	2·00	4·25	☐	☐
	Set of 2 Gutter Pairs	.. ..	5·50		☐	

1001 Fencing   **1002** Hurdling

1003 Diving   **1004** Rugby

World Student Games, Sheffield (Nos. 1564/6) and World Cup Rugby Championship, London (No. 1567)

1991 (11 JUNE) *Phosphorised paper. Perf* 14½ × 14

1564	**1001**	22p multicoloured	..	50	50	☐	☐
1565	**1002**	26p multicoloured	..	70	70	☐	☐
1566	**1003**	31p multicoloured	..	85	85	☐	☐
1567	**1004**	37p multicoloured	..	1·00	1·00	☐	☐
	Set of 4	.. ..		2·75	2·75	☐	☐
	First Day Cover	.. ..			4·00	☐	
	Presentation Pack	.. ..		3·50		☐	
	PHQ Cards (set of 4)	.. ..		1·25	4·25	☐	☐
	Set of 4 Gutter Pairs	.. ..		5·50		☐	

1005 "Silver Jubilee"   **1006** "Mme Alfred Carrière"

1007 *Rosa moyesii*   **1008** "Harvest Fayre"

1009 "Mutabilis"

9th World Congress of Roses, Belfast

1991 (16 JULY) *Phosphorised paper. Perf* 14½ × 14

1568	**1005**	22p multicoloured	..	75	50	☐	☐
1569	**1006**	26p multicoloured	..	80	80	☐	☐
1570	**1007**	31p multicoloured	..	85	85	☐	☐
1571	**1008**	33p multicoloured	..	95	95	☐	☐
1572	**1009**	37p multicoloured	..	1·10	1·25	☐	☐
	Set of 5	.. .. ..		4·00	4·00	☐	☐
	First Day Cover	.. .. ..			4·50		☐
	Presentation Pack	.. ..		4·50		☐	
	PHQ Cards (set of 5)	.. ..		1·50	4·50	☐	☐
	Set of 5 Gutter Pairs	.. ..		8·00		☐	

1010 Iguanodon   **1011** Stegosaurus

1012 Tyrannosaurus   **1013** Protoceratops

1014 Triceratops

150th Anniversary of Dinosaurs' Identification by Owen

1991 (20 Aug.) *Phosphorised paper. Perf 14½ × 14*

1573	**1010**	22p multicoloured	..	75	50	☐	☐
1574	**1011**	26p multicoloured	..	80	80	☐	☐
1575	**1012**	31p multicoloured	..	85	85	☐	☐
1576	**1013**	33p multicoloured	..	95	95	☐	☐
1577	**1014**	37p multicoloured	..	1·10	1·25	☐	☐
		Set of 5	.. .. ..	4·00	4·00	☐	☐
		First Day Cover	.. ..		4·50		☐
		Presentation Pack	.. ..	4·50		☐	
		PHQ Cards (set of 5)	.. ..	1·50	4·50	☐	☐
		Set of 5 Gutter Pairs	.. ..	8·00		☐	

1015 Map of 1816

1016 Map of 1906

1017 Map of 1959

1018 Map of 1991

Bicentenary of Ordnance Survey. Maps of Hamstreet, Kent

1991 (17 Sept.) *Phosphorised paper. Perf 14½ × 14*

1578	**1015**	24p multicoloured	..	50	50	☐	☐
1579	**1016**	28p multicoloured	..	70	70	☐	☐
1580	**1017**	33p multicoloured	..	85	85	☐	☐
1581	**1018**	39p multicoloured	..	1·00	1·00	☐	☐
		Set of 4	.. .. ..	2·75	2·75	☐	☐
		First Day Cover	.. ..		4·25		☐
		Presentation Pack	..	4·00		☐	
		PHQ Cards (set of 4)	.. ..	1·10	4·25	☐	☐
		Set of 4 Gutter Pairs	.. ..	5·50		☐	

1019 Adoration of the Magi

1020 Mary and Baby Jesus in the Stable

1021 The Holy Family and Angel

1022 The Annunciation

1023 The Flight into Egypt

Christmas. Illuminated Manuscripts from the Bodleian Library, Oxford

1991 (12 Nov.) *One phosphor band (18p) or phosphorised paper (others)*

1582	**1019**	18p multicoloured	..	70	40	☐	☐
1583	**1020**	24p multicoloured	..	80	50	☐	☐
1584	**1021**	28p multicoloured	..	85	1·00	☐	☐
1585	**1022**	33p multicoloured	..	95	1·10	☐	☐
1586	**1023**	39p multicoloured	..	1·10	1·40	☐	☐
		Set of 5	.. .. ..	4·00	4·00	☐	☐
		First Day Cover	.. ..		4·50		☐
		Presentation Pack	..	4·25		☐	
		PHQ Cards (set of 5)	.. ..	1·50	4·50	☐	☐
		Set of 5 Gutter Pairs	.. ..	8·00		☐	

Collectors Pack 1991

1991 (12 Nov.) *Comprises Nos.* 1531/5, 1546/9 *and* 1560/86.

	Collectors Pack	30·00	☐

Post Office Yearbook

1991 *Comprises Nos.* 1531/5, 1546/9 *and* 1560/86. *in hardback book with slip case.*

	Yearbook	40·00	☐

1024 Fallow Deer in Scottish Forest

1025 Hare on North Yorkshire Moors

1026 Fox in the Fens

1027 Redwing and Home Counties Village

1028 Welsh Mountain Sheep in Snowdonia

1031 Key

1032 Model Car and Cigarette Cards

1033 Compass and Map

1034 Pocket Watch

1035 1d. Red Stamp and Pen

1036 Pearl Necklace

1037 Marbles

1038 Bucket, Spade and Starfish

The Four Seasons. Wintertime

1992 (14 JAN.) *One phosphor band* (18p) *or phosphorised paper* (*others*)

1587	**1024**	18p multicoloured	..	30	35	☐ ☐
1588	**1025**	24p multicoloured	..	40	45	☐ ☐
1589	**1026**	28p multicoloured	..	45	50	☐ ☐
1590	**1027**	33p multicoloured	..	50	55	☐ ☐
1591	**1028**	39p multicoloured	..	60	65	☐ ☐
		Set of 5		2·00	2·25	☐ ☐
		First Day Cover			4·75	☐
		Presentation Pack		2·50		☐
		PHQ Cards (*set of 5*)		1·50	4·50	☐ ☐
		Set of 5 Gutter Pairs ..		4·25		☐

1029 Flower Spray

1030 Double Locket

T **1029**/**38** were printed together, *se-tenant*, in booklet panes of 10, the backgrounds of the stamps forming a composite design.

Greetings Stamps. "Memories".

1992 (28 JAN.) *Two phosphor bands*

1592	**1029**	(1st) multicoloured	..	40	45	☐ ☐
		a. *Booklet pane. Nos.*				
		1592/1601 plus				
		12 half stamp-size				
		labels		3·50		☐
1593	**1030**	(1st) multicoloured	..	40	45	☐ ☐
1594	**1031**	(1st) multicoloured	..	40	45	☐ ☐
1595	**1032**	(1st) multicoloured	..	40	45	☐ ☐
1596	**1033**	(1st) multicoloured	..	40	45	☐ ☐
1597	**1034**	(1st) multicoloured	..	40	45	☐ ☐
1598	**1035**	(1st) multicoloured	..	40	45	☐ ☐
1599	**1036**	(1st) multicoloured	..	40	45	☐ ☐
1600	**1037**	(1st) multicoloured	..	40	45	☐ ☐
1601	**1038**	(1st) multicoloured	..	40	45	☐ ☐
		Set of 10		3·50	4·00	☐ ☐
		Presentation Pack		4·00		☐
		First Day Cover			7·00	☐

1039 Queen Elizabeth in Coronation Robes and Parliamentary Emblem

1040 Queen Elizabeth in Garter Robes and Archiepiscopal Arms

1041 Queen Elizabeth with Baby Prince Andrew and Royal Arms

1042 Queen Elizabeth at Trooping the Colour and Service Emblems

1043 Queen Elizabeth and Commonwealth Emblem

Nos. 1602/6 were printed together, *se-tenant*, in horizontal strips of 5 throughout the sheet, forming a composite design.

40th Anniversary of Accession

1992 (6 Feb.) *Two phosphor bands. Perf* $14\frac{1}{2} \times 14$.

1602	**1039**	24p multicoloured	..	40	45	☐ ☐
		a. Horiz strip of 5.				
		Nos. 1602/6	..	1·75	2·00	☐ ☐
1603	**1040**	24p multicoloured	..	40	45	☐ ☐
1604	**1041**	24p multicoloured	..	40	45	☐ ☐
1605	**1042**	24p multicoloured	..	40	45	☐ ☐
1606	**1043**	24p multicoloured	..	40	45	☐ ☐
		Set of 5	..	1·75	2·00	☐ ☐
		First Day Cover	..		4·00	☐
		Presentation Pack ..		2·25		☐
		PHQ Cards (set of 5)..		1·50	4·25	☐ ☐
		Gutter strip of 10 ..		3·75		☐

1044 Tennyson in 1888 and "The Beguiling of Merlin" (Sir Edward Burne-Jones)

1045 Tennyson in 1864 and "I am Sick of the Shadows" (John Waterhouse)

1046 Tennyson in 1856 and "April Love" (Arthur Hughes)

1047 Tennyson as a Young Man and "Mariana" (Dante Gabriel Rossetti)

Death Centenary of Alfred, Lord Tennyson (poet)

1992 (10 Mar.) *Phosphorised paper. Perf* $14\frac{1}{2} \times 14$

1607	**1044**	24p multicoloured	..	40	45	☐ ☐
1608	**1045**	28p multicoloured	..	45	50	☐ ☐
1609	**1046**	33p multicoloured	..	50	55	☐ ☐
1610	**1047**	39p multicoloured	..	60	65	☐ ☐
		Set of 4	..	1·75	1·90	☐ ☐
		First Day Cover	..		4·00	☐
		Presentation Pack ..		2·40		☐
		PHQ Cards (set of 4)..		1·40	4·50	☐
		Set of 4 Gutter Pairs ..		3·75		☐

CARRICKFERGUS CASTLE

1048 Carrickfergus Castle

1992 (24 Mar.) *Designs as Nos. 1410/13, but showing Queen's head in silhouette as T* **1048**.

1611	**1048**	£1 bottle green and gold†	1·50	1·50	☐ ☐
1612	**882**	£1·50 maroon and gold†	2·25	2·25	☐ ☐
1613	**883**	£2 indigo and gold† ..	3·00	3·00	☐ ☐
1614	**884**	£5 deep brown and gold†	7·50	7·50	☐ ☐
		Set of 4	13·00	13·00	☐ ☐
		First Day Cover		30·00	☐
		Presentation Pack	14·50		☐
		Set of 4 Gutter Pairs	27·00		☐

†The Queen's head on these stamps is printed in optically variable ink which changes colour from gold to green when viewed from different angles.

These stamps show a larger oval-shaped perforation hole at the centre of each vertical side.

1049 British Olympic Association Logo (Olympic Games, Barcelona)

1050 British Paralympic Association Symbol (Paralympics '92, Barcelona)

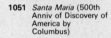

1051 *Santa Maria* (500th Anniv of Discovery of America by Columbus)

1052 *Kaisei* (cadet sailing ship) (Grand Regatta Columbus, 1992)

1053 British Pavilion, ''EXPO '92'', Seville

Nos. 1615/16 were printed together, *se-tenant*, in horizontal pairs throughout the sheet.

Europa. International Events

1992 (7 APR.) *Phosphorised paper. Perf* 14 × 14½

1615	**1049**	24p multicoloured	..	40	45	☐ ☐
		a. Horiz pair.				
		Nos. 1615/16	..	80	90	☐ ☐
1616	**1050**	24p multicoloured		40	45	☐ ☐
1617	**1051**	24p multicoloured		40	45	☐ ☐
1618	**1052**	39p multicoloured		60	65	☐ ☐
1619	**1053**	39p multicoloured		60	65	☐ ☐
		Set of 5	.. .. ..	2·10	2·50	☐
		First Day Cover ..	..		4·50	☐
		Presentation Pack	..	2·50		☐
		PHQ Cards (set of 5) ..		1·50	4·50	☐ ☐
		Set of 4 Gutter Pairs ..	..	4·50		☐

1054 Pikeman

1055 Drummer

1056 Musketeer

1057 Standard Bearer

350th Anniversary of the Civil War

1992 (16 JUNE) *Phosphorised paper. Perf* 14½ × 14

1620	**1054**	24p multicoloured	..	40	45	☐ ☐
1621	**1055**	28p multicoloured		45	50	☐ ☐
1622	**1056**	33p multicoloured		50	55	☐ ☐
1623	**1057**	39p multicoloured		60	65	☐ ☐
		Set of 4	.. .. ..	1·75	2·00	☐ ☐
		First Day Cover ..	.. ..		4·00	☐
		Presentation Pack	..	2·40		☐
		PHQ Cards (set of 4) ..		1·40	4·50	☐ ☐
		Set of 4 Gutter Pairs ..		3·75		☐

1058 *The Yeoman of the Guard*

1059 *The Gondoliers*

1060 *The Mikado*

1061 *The Pirates of Penzance*

1062 Iolanthe

1067 European Star

50th Birth Anniversary of Sir Arthur Sullivan (composer). Gilbert and Sullivan Operas

1992 (21 July) One phosphor band (18p) or phosphorised paper (others). Perf 14½ × 14

1624	**1058**	18p multicoloured	..	30	35	☐	☐
1625	**1059**	24p multicoloured	..	40	45	☐	☐
1626	**1060**	28p multicoloured	..	45	50	☐	☐
1627	**1061**	33p multicoloured	..	50	55	☐	☐
1628	**1062**	39p multicoloured	..	60	65	☐	☐
		Set of 5	..	2·00	2·25	☐	☐
		First Day Cover			4·75		☐
		Presentation Pack		2·50		☐	
		PHQ Cards (set of 5)		1·50	5·00	☐	☐
		Set of 5 Gutter Pairs ..		4·25		☐	

Single European Market

1992 (13 Oct.) Phosphorised paper

1633	**1067**	24p multicoloured	..	40	45	☐	☐
		First Day Cover			1·00		☐
		Presentation Pack		85		☐	
		PHQ Card		35	1·40	☐	☐
		Gutter Pair		85		☐	

1063 "Acid Rain Kills"

1064 "Ozone Layer"

1068 Angel Gabriel

1069 Madonna and Child

1065 "Greenhouse Effect"

1066 "Bird of Hope"

1070 The Magi: Gold

1071 The Shepherds

Protection of the Environment. Children's Paintings

1992 (15 Sept.) Phosphorised paper. Perf 14 × 14½

1629	**1063**	24p multicoloured	..	40	45	☐	☐
1630	**1064**	28p multicoloured	..	45	50	☐	☐
1631	**1065**	33p multicoloured	..	50	55	☐	☐
1632	**1066**	39p multicoloured	..	60	65	☐	☐
		Set of 4	..	1·75	1·90	☐	☐
		First Day Cover			2·75		☐
		Presentation Pack		2·40		☐	
		PHQ Cards (set of 4)		1·40	4·25	☐	☐
		Set of 4 Gutter Pairs ..		3·75		☐	

1072 The Magi: Frankincense and Myrrh

Christmas. Stained Glass Windows

1992 (10 Nov.) *One phosphor band (18p) or phosphorised paper (others)*

1634	**1068**	18p multicoloured	..	30	35	☐ ☐
1635	**1069**	24p multicoloured	..	40	45	☐ ☐
1636	**1070**	28p multicoloured	..	45	50	☐ ☐
1637	**1071**	33p multicoloured	..	50	55	☐ ☐
1638	**1072**	39p multicoloured	..	60	65	☐ ☐
		Set of 5		2·00	2·25	☐ ☐
		First Day Cover			3·00	☐
		Presentation Pack		2·50		☐
		PHQ Cards (set of 5)		1·50	4·50	☐ ☐
		Set of 5 Gutter Pairs		4·25		☐

Collectors Pack 1992

1992 (10 Nov.) *Comprises Nos.* 1587/91, 1602/10 *and* 1615/38.

	Collectors Pack	18·00		☐

Post Office Yearbook

1992 (11 Nov.) *Comprises Nos.* 1587/91, 1602/10 *and* 1615/38 *in hardback book with slip case.*

	Yearbook	29·00		☐

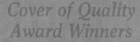

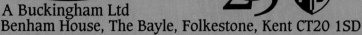

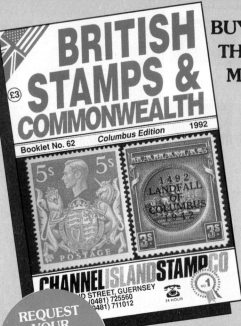

ERFORATION AND WATERMARK. All the following egional stamps are perforated 15×14 and are watermarked Type **179**, unless otherwise stated.

For listing of First Day Covers see pages 110/11.

Northern Ireland

1	N 2	N 3	N 4

958–67

11	N 1	3d	lilac	20	10 ☐ ☐
		p.	*One centre phosphor band* ..	20	15 ☐ ☐
12		4d	blue	20	15 ☐ ☐
		p.	*Two phosphor bands*	20	15 ☐ ☐
13	N 2	6d	purple	20	20 ☐ ☐
14		9d	bronze-green (2 phosphor bands)	30	50 ☐ ☐
15	N 3	1s 3d	green	30	50 ☐ ☐
16		1s 6d	blue (2 phosphor bands)	30	50 ☐ ☐

968–69 *One centre phosphor band (Nos. NI8/9) or two hosphor bands (others). No wmk*

17	N 1	4d	blue	20	15 ☐ ☐
18		4d	sepia	20	15 ☐ ☐
19		4d	vermilion ..	20	20 ☐ ☐
110		5d	blue	20	20 ☐ ☐
111	N 3	1s 6d	blue	2·50	3·00 ☐ ☐
		Presentation Pack (comprises Nos. NI1p, NI4/6, NI8/10) ..	3·00	☐

ecimal Currency

971–91 *Type N 4. No wmk*

(a) Printed in photogravure with phosphor bands

12	2½p	magenta (1 centre band) ..	75	25 ☐ ☐
113	3p	ultramarine (2 bands) ..	40	15 ☐ ☐
14	3p	ultramarine (1 centre band)	20	15 ☐ ☐
15	3½p	olive-grey (2 bands) ..	20	20 ☐ ☐
16	3½p	olive-grey (1 centre band)	20	25 ☐ ☐
17	4½p	grey-blue (2 bands) ..	25	25 ☐ ☐
118	5p	violet (2 bands) ..	1·50	1·50 ☐ ☐
19	5½p	violet (2 bands) ..	20	20 ☐ ☐
20	5½p	violet (1 centre band) ..	20	20 ☐ ☐
121	6½p	blue (1 centre band) ..	20	20 ☐ ☐

NI22	7p	brown (1 centre band)	35	25 ☐ ☐
NI23	7½p	chestnut (2 bands) ..	2·50	2·50 ☐ ☐
NI24	8p	rosine (2 bands) ..	30	30 ☐ ☐
NI25	8½p	yellow-green (2 bands)	30	30 ☐ ☐
NI26	9p	violet (2 bands)	30	30 ☐ ☐
NI27	10p	orange-brown (2 bands)	35	35 ☐ ☐
NI28	10p	orange-brown (1 centre band)	35	35 ☐ ☐
NI29	10½p	blue (2 bands)	40	40 ☐ ☐
NI30	11p	scarlet (2 bands)	40	40 ☐ ☐

(b) Printed in photogravure on phosphorised paper

NI31	12p	yellowish green ..	50	45 ☐ ☐
NI32	13½p	purple-brown	60	70 ☐ ☐
NI33	15p	ultramarine	60	50 ☐ ☐

(c) Printed in lithography. Perf 14 (11½p, 12½p, 14p, (No. NI38), 15½p, 16p, 18p, (No. NI45), 19½p, 20½p, 22p, (No. NI52), 26p, (No. NI58), 28p (No. NI60), or 15×14 (others).

NI34	11½p	drab (1 side band)	1·00	60 ☐ ☐
NI35	12p	brt emer (1 side band) ..	50	50 ☐ ☐
NI36	12½p	light emer (1 side band)..	50	40 ☐ ☐
		a. Perf 15 × 14 ..	4·50	4·50 ☐ ☐
NI37	13p	pale chest (1 side band)..	60	35 ☐ ☐
NI38	14p	grey-blue (phosphorised paper)	70	50 ☐ ☐
NI39	14p	dp blue (1 centre band) ..	40	35 ☐ ☐
NI40	15p	brt blue (1 centre band) ..	45	30 ☐ ☐
NI41	15½p	pale violet (phosphorised paper)	1·00	65 ☐ ☐
NI42	16p	drab (phosphorised paper)	1·00	1·00 ☐ ☐
		a. Perf 15 × 14 ..	7·00	1·00 ☐ ☐
NI43	17p	grey-blue (phosphorised paper).. ..	80	40 ☐ ☐
NI44	17p	deep blue (1 centre band)	30	35 ☐ ☐
NI45	18p	dp violet (phosphorised paper)	80	80 ☐ ☐
NI46	18p	olive-grey (phosphorised paper)	80	70 ☐ ☐
NI47	18p	brt grn (1 centre band)	30	35 ☐ ☐
NI48	19p	bright orange-red (phosphorised paper)	60	60 ☐ ☐
NI49	19½p	olive-grey (phosphorised paper)	2·00	2·00 ☐ ☐
NI50	20p	brownish black (phosphorised paper)	30	30 ☐ ☐
NI51	20½p	ultramarine (phosphorised paper)	2·00	2·00 ☐ ☐
NI52	22p	blue (phosphorised paper)	90	1·10 ☐ ☐
NI53	22p	yellow-green (phosphorised paper)	85	85 ☐ ☐
NI54	22p	bright orange-red (phosphorised paper)	85	40 ☐ ☐
NI55	23p	bright green (phosphorised paper)	80	80 ☐ ☐
NI56	24p	Indian red (phosphorised paper)	70	70 ☐ ☐
NI57	24p	chestnut (phosphorised paper)	40	45 ☐ ☐

NI58	26p rosine (phosphorised				
	paper)	90	90	☐	☐
	a. Perf 15 × 14	2·50	2·50	☐	☐
NI59	26p drab (phosphorised				
	paper)	40	45	☐	☐
NI60	28p deep violet-blue				
	(phosphorised paper)	1·00	1·00	☐	☐
	a. Perf 15 × 14	80	80	☐	☐
NI61	28p deep bluish grey				
	(phosphorised paper)	45	50	☐	☐
NI62	31p bright purple				
	(phosphorised paper)	1·10	1·10	☐	☐
NI63	32p greenish blue				
	(phosphorised paper)	1·10	1·10	☐	☐
NI64	34p deep bluish grey				
	(phosphorised paper)	1·00	1·00	☐	☐
NI65	37p rosine (phosphorised				
	paper)	60	65	☐	☐
NI66	39p bright mauve				
	(phosphorised paper)	60	65	☐	☐

Presentation Pack (*contains* 2½p (NI12), 3p (NI13), 5p (NI18), 7½p (NI23)) .. — 4·00 — ☐

Presentation Pack (*contains* 3p (NI14), 3½p (NI15), 5½p (NI19), 8p (NI24) *later with* 4½p (NI17) *added*) .. .. — 3·00 — ☐

Presentation Pack (*contains* 6½p (NI21), 8½p (NI25), 10p (NI27), 11p (NI30)) .. — 1·75 — ☐

Presentation Pack (*contains* 7p (NI22), 9p (NI26), 10½p (NI29), 11½p (NI34), 12p (NI31), 13½p (NI32), 14p (NI38), 15p (NI33), 18p (NI45), 22p (NI52)) .. — 6·00 — ☐

Presentation Pack (*contains* 10p (NI28), 12½p (NI36), 16p (NI42), 20½p (NI51), 26p (NI58), 28p (NI60)) .. — 5·00 — ☐

Presentation Pack (*contains* 10p (NI28), 13p (NI37), 16p (NI42a), 17p (NI43), 22p (NI53), 26p (NI58), 28p (NI60), 31p (NI62)) .. — 8·00 — ☐

Presentation Pack (*contains* 12p (NI35), 13p (NI37), 17p (NI43), 20½p (NI46), 22p (NI53), 26p (NI58a), 28p (NI60a), 31p (NI62)) .. — 8·00 — ☐

Presentation Pack (*contains* 14p, 19p, 23p, 32p *from Northern Ireland, Scotland and Wales* (*Nos.* NI39, NI48, NI55, NI63, S54, S61, S66, S75, W40, W50, W57, W66)) — 6·00 — ☐

Presentation Pack (*contains* 15p, 20p, 24p, 34p *from Northern Ireland, Scotland and Wales* (*Nos.* NI40, NI50, NI56, NI64, S56, S63, S68, S76, W41, W52, W58, W67)) — 5·00 — ☐

Presentation Pack (*contains* 17p, 22p, 26p, 37p, *from Northern Ireland, Scotland and Wales* (*Nos.* NI44, NI54, NI59, NI65, S58, S65, S71, S77, W45, W56, W62, W68)) — 5·00 — ☐

Presentation Pack (*contains* 18p, 24p, 28p, 39p *from Northern Ireland, Scotland and Wales* (*Nos.* NI47, NI57, NI61, NI66, S60, S69, S73, S78, W48, W59, W64, W69)) — 5·50 — ☐

Scotland

| 1 | S 2 | S 3 | S 4 |

1958—67

1	S 1	3d lilac	20	15	☐ ☐
		p. Two phosphor bands	14·00	1·00	☐ ☐
		pa. One side band	20	25	☐ ☐
		pb. One centre band	20	15	☐ ☐
2		4d blue	20	10	☐ ☐
		p. Two phosphor bands	20	20	☐ ☐
3	S 2	6d purple ..	20	15	☐ ☐
		p. Two phosphor bands	20	25	☐ ☐
4		9d bronze-green (2 phosphor bands)	30	30	☐ ☐
5	S 3	1s 3d green	30	30	☐ ☐
		p. Two phosphor bands	30	30	☐ ☐
6		1s 6d blue (2 phosphor bands)	35	30	☐ ☐

No. S1pa exists with the phosphor band at the left or right of the stamp.

1967—70 One centre phosphor band (Nos. S7, S9/10) or two phosphor bands (others). No wmk

7	S 1	3d lilac	10	15	☐ ☐
8		4d blue	10	15	☐ ☐
9		4d sepia	10	10	☐ ☐
10		4d vermilion ..	10	10	☐ ☐
11		5d blue	20	10	☐ ☐
12	S 2	9d bronze-green ..	5·00	5·50	☐ ☐
13	S 3	1s 6d blue ..	1·40	1·00	☐ ☐
		Presentation Pack (containing Nos. S3, S5p, S7, S9/13) ..	13·00		☐

Decimal Currency

1971—91 Type S 4. No wmk

(a) Printed in photogravure by Harrison and Sons with phosphor bands. Perf 15 × 14.

14	2½p magenta (1 centre band)	25	15	☐ ☐
15	3p ultramarine (2 bands) ..	30	15	☐ ☐
16	3p ultramarine (1 centre band)	15	15	☐ ☐
17	3½p olive-grey (2 bands) ..	20	20	☐ ☐
18	3½p ol-grey (1 centre band)	20	20	☐ ☐
19	4½p grey-blue (2 bands) ..	25	20	☐ ☐
20	5p violet (2 bands) ..	1·50	1·50	☐ ☐
21	5½p violet (2 bands) ..	20	20	☐ ☐
22	5½p violet (1 centre band)	20	20	☐ ☐
23	6½p blue (1 centre band) ..	20	20	☐ ☐
S24	7p brown (1 centre band)	25	25	☐ ☐
S25	7½p chestnut (2 bands) ..	2·00	2·00	☐ ☐
S26	8p rosine (2 bands)	30	40	☐ ☐
S27	8½p yellow-green (2 bands)	30	30	☐ ☐
S28	9p violet (2 bands) ..	30	30	☐ ☐
S29	10p orange-brown (2 bands)	35	30	☐ ☐
S30	10p orange-brown (1 centre band)	35	35	☐ ☐
S31	10½p blue (2 bands) ..	45	35	☐ ☐
S32	11p scarlet (2 bands) ..	45	35	☐ ☐

(b) Printed in photogravure by Harrison and Sons on phosphorised paper. Perf 15 × 14

S33	12p yellowish green	50	30	☐ ☐
S34	13½p purple-brown	60	65	☐ ☐
S35	15p ultramarine	60	45	☐ ☐

(c) Printed in lithography by John Waddington. One side phosphor band (11½p, 12p, 12½p, 13p) or phosphorised paper (others). Perf 13½ × 14

S36	11½p drab	85	60	☐ ☐
S37	12p bright emerald	80	70	☐ ☐
S38	12½p light emerald	50	40	☐ ☐
S39	13p pale chestnut	60 .	30	☐ ☐
S40	14p grey-blue	60	50	☐ ☐
S41	15½p pale violet	70	65	☐ ☐
S42	16p drab	70	45	☐ ☐
S43	17p grey-blue	3·25	2·00	☐ ☐
S44	18p deep violet	1·00	90	☐ ☐
S45	19½p olive-grey	2·00	2·25	☐ ☐
S46	20½p ultramarine	3·75	3·75	☐ ☐
S47	22p blue	80	1·10	☐ ☐
S48	22p yellow-green	1·00	80	☐ ☐
S49	26p rosine	90	80	☐ ☐
S50	28p deep violet-blue	1·00	80	☐ ☐
S51	31p bright purple	1·40	1·10	☐ ☐

(d) Printed in lithography by Questa. Perf 15 × 14

S52	12p brt emer (1 side band) ..	60	60	☐ ☐
S53	13p pale chest (1 side band) ..	60	30	☐ ☐
S54	14p dp blue (1 centre band)	40	30	☐ ☐
S55	14p deep blue (1 side band) ..	80	80	☐ ☐
S56	15p bright blue (1 centre band)	50	30	☐ ☐
S57	17p grey-blue (phosphorised paper)	3·50	2·00	☐ ☐
S58	17p dp blue (1 centre band) ..	30	35	☐ ☐
S59	18p olive-grey (phosphorised paper)	1·00	90	☐ ☐
S60	18p brt green (1 centre band)	30	35	☐ ☐
S61	19p bright orange-red (phosphorised paper)	60	45	☐ ☐
S62	19p brt orange-red (2 bands)	1·40	1·40	☐ ☐
S63	20p brownish black (phosphorised paper)	60	30	☐ ☐
S64	22p yell-grn (phosphorised paper)	80	80	☐ ☐
S65	22p bright orange-red (phosphorised paper)	90	40	☐ ☐
S66	23p brt green (phosphorised paper)	90	80	☐ ☐
S67	23p bright green (2 bands) ..	4·50	4·50	☐ ☐

S68	24p	Indian red (phosphorised paper)	70	70	□	□
S69	24p	chestnut (phosphorised paper)	40	45	□	□
S70	26p	rosine (phosphorised paper)	1·90	1·90	□	□
S71	26p	drab (phosphorised paper)	40	45	□	□
S72	28p	deep violet-blue (phosphorised paper) ..	85	75	□	□
S73	28p	deep bluish grey (phosphorised paper) ..	45	50	□	□
S74	31p	bright purple (phosphorised paper) ..	1·50	1·50	□	□
S75	32p	greenish blue (phosphorised paper) ..	1·10	90	□	□
S76	34p	deep bluish grey (phosphorised paper) ..	1·00	90	□	□
S77	37p	rosine (phosphorised paper)	60	65	□	□
S78	39p	bright mauve (phosphorised paper) ..	60	65	□	□

Presentation Pack (contains 2½p (S14), 3p (S15), 5p (S20), 7½p (S25)) .. .. 4·00 □

Presentation Pack (contains 3p (S16), 3½p (S17), 5½p (S21), 8p (S26) *later with* 4½p (S19) *added)* .. .. 3·00 □

Presentation Pack (contains 6½p (S23), 8½p (S27), 10p (S29), 11p (S32)) .. .. 1·75 □

Presentation Pack (contains 7p (S24), 9p (S28), 10½p (S31), 11½p (S36), 12p (S33), 13½p (S34), 14p (S40), 15p (S35), 18p (S44), 22p (S47)) .. 6·00 □

Presentation Pack (contains 10p (S30), 12½p (S38), 16p (S42), 20½p (S46), 26p (S49), 28p (S50)) .. .. 6·50 □

Presentation Pack (contains 10p (S30), 13p (S39), 16p (S42), 17p (S43), 22p (S48), 26p (S49), 28p (S50), 31p (S51)) .. .. 8·00 □

Presentation Pack (contains 12p, (S52), 13p (S53), 17p (S57), 18p (S59), 22p (S64), 26p (S70), 28p (S72), 31p (S74)) .. .. 8·00 □

For combined packs containing values from all three Regions see under Northern Ireland.

W 1   W 2   W 3   W 4

1958–67

No.	Type	Description					
W1	W 1	3d lilac	20	10	☐	☐
		p. One centre phosphor band ..	20	15	☐	☐
W2		4d blue	20	15	☐	☐
		p. Two phosphor bands	20	15	☐	☐
W3	W 2	6d purple	40	20	☐	☐
W4		9d bronze-green (2 phosphor bands)	30	35	☐	☐
W5	W 3	1s 3d green	30	30	☐	☐
W6		1s 6d blue (2 phosphor bands)	35	30	☐	☐

1967–69 One centre phosphor band (Nos. W7, W9/10) or two phosphor bands (others). No wmk

No.	Type	Description					
W7	W 1	3d lilac	20	10	☐	☐
W8		4d blue	20	10	☐	☐
W9		4d sepia	20	10	☐	☐
W10		4d vermilion	20	20	☐	☐
W11		5d blue	20	10	☐	☐
W12	W 3	1s 6d blue	3·00	3·00	☐	☐
		Presentation Pack (comprises Nos. W4, W6/7, W9/11) ..	2·50		☐	

Decimal Currency

1971–92 Type W 4. No wmk

(a) Printed in photogravure with phosphor bands

No.	Description				
W13	2½p magenta (1 centre band)	20	15	☐	☐
W14	3p ultramarine (2 bands) ..	25	15	☐	☐
W15	3p ultramarine (1 centre band)	20	20	☐	☐
W16	3½p olive-grey (2 bands) ..	20	25	☐	☐
W17	3½p olive-grey (1 centre band)	20	25	☐	☐
W18	4½p grey-blue (2 bands) ..	25	20	☐	☐
W19	5p violet (2 bands)	1·50	1·50	☐	☐
W20	5½p violet (2 bands)	20	25	☐	☐
W21	5½p violet (1 centre band) ..	20	25	☐	☐
W22	6½p blue (1 centre band) ..	20	20	☐	☐
W23	7p brown (1 centre band) ..	25	25	☐	☐
W24	7½p chestnut (2 bands) ..	2·00	2·25	☐	☐
W25	8p rosine (2 bands)	30	30	☐	☐
W26	8½p yellow-green (2 bands) ..	30	30	☐	☐
W27	9p violet (2 bands)	30	30	☐	☐
W28	10p orange-brown (2 bands)	35	30	☐	☐
W29	10p orange-brown (1 centre band)	35	30	☐	☐
W30	10½p blue (2 bands)	40	35	☐	☐
W31	11p scarlet (2 bands)	40	45	☐	☐

(b) Printed in photogravure on phosphorised paper

No.	Description				
W32	12p yellowish green	50	45	☐	☐
W33	13½p purple-brown	60	70	☐	☐
W34	15p ultramarine	60	50	☐	☐

(c) Printed in lithography. Perf 14 (11½p, 12½p, 14p (No. W39), 15½p, 16p, 18p, (No. W42), 19½p, 20½p, 22p, (No. W58), 26p, (No. W61), 28p) or 15 × 14 (others).

No.	Description				
W35	11½p drab (1 side band) ..	85	60	☐	☐
W36	12p brt emer (1 side band) ..	1·40	1·10	☐	☐
W37	12½p light emer (1 side band)..	60	60	☐	☐
	a. Perf 15 × 14	6·00	4·50	☐	☐
W38	13p pale chest (1 side band)..	50	35	☐	☐
W39	14p grey-blue (phosphorised paper)	65	50	☐	☐
W40	14p dp blue (1 centre band) ..	35	30	☐	☐
W41	15p brt blue (1 centre band)..	25	30	☐	☐
W42	15½p pale violet (phosphorised paper)	80	65	☐	☐
W43	16p drab (phosphorised paper)	1·50	1·25	☐	☐
	a. Perf 15 × 14 ..	1·50	1·25	☐	☐
W44	17p grey-blue (phosphorised paper)	70	55	☐	☐
W45	17p deep blue (1 centre band)	30	35	☐	☐
W46	18p deep violet (phosphorised paper)	80	75	☐	☐
W47	18p olive-grey (phosphorised paper)	1·00	45	☐	☐
W48	18p brt grn (1 centre band)	30	35	☐	☐
W49	18p brt green (1 side band)	1·10	1·10	☐	☐
W50	19p bright orange-red (phosphorised paper) ..	60	45	☐	☐
W51	19½p olive-grey (phosphorised paper)	2·00	2·00	☐	☐
W52	20p brownish black (phosphorised paper)	30	30	☐	☐
W53	20½p ultramarine (phosphorised paper)	2·00	2·00	☐	☐
W54	22p blue (phosphorised paper)	1·00	1·10	☐	☐
W55	22p yell-green (phosphorised paper)	80	50	☐	☐
W56	22p bright orange-red (phosphorised paper)	35	40	☐	☐
W57	23p brt green (phosphorised paper)	80	50	☐	☐
W58	24p Indian red (phosphorised paper)	40	45	☐	☐
W59	24p chestnut (phosphorised paper)	40	45	☐	☐
W60	24p chestnut (2 bands) ..	1·10	1·10	☐	☐

W61	26p	rosine (phosphorised paper)	90	80	☐	☐
		a. Perf 15 × 14	3·50	3·50	☐	☐
W62	26p	drab (phosphorised paper)	40	45	☐	☐
W63	28p	dp viol-blue (phosphorised paper)	1·00	80	☐	☐
		a. Perf 15 × 14	70	65	☐	☐
W64	28p	deep bluish grey (phosphorised paper)	45	50	☐	☐
W65	31p	brt purple (phosphorised paper)	1·00	70	☐	☐
W66	32p	greenish blue (phosphorised paper)	1·10	75	☐	☐
W67	34p	deep bluish grey (phosphorised paper) ..	55	55	☐	☐
W68	37p	rosine (phosphorised paper)	60	65	☐	☐
W69	39p	bright mauve (phosphorised paper)	60	65	☐	☐

Presentation Pack (contains 2½p (W13), 3p (W14), 5p (W19), 7½p (W24)) .. .. 4·00 ☐

Presentation Pack (contains 3p (W15), 3½p (W16), 5½p (W20), 8p (W25), later with 4½p (W18) added) .. .. 3·00 ☐

Presentation Pack (contains 6½p (W22), 8½p (W26), 10p (W28), 11p (W31)) .. .. 1·75 ☐

Presentation Pack (contains 7p (W23), 9p (W27), 10½p (W30), 11½p (W35), 12p (W32), 13½p (W33), 14p (W39), 15p (W34), 18p (W46), 22p (W53)) .. 6·00 ☐

Presentation Pack (contains 10p (W29), 12½p (W37), 16p (W43), 20½p (W53), 26p (W61), 28p (W63)) .. 6·50 ☐

Presentation Pack (contains 10p (W29), 13p (W38), 16p (W43a), 17p (W44), 22p (W55), 26p (W61), 28p (W63), 31p (W65)) .. 8·50 ☐

Presentation Pack (contains 12p (W36), 13p (W38), 17p (W44), 18p (W47), 22p (W55), 26p (W61a), 28p (W63a), 31p (W65)) .. 8·00 ☐

For combined packs containing values from all three Regions see under Northern Ireland.

ISLE OF MAN

Regional Issues

1   2   3

1958–67 *Wmk* **179**   *Perf* 15×14

1	1	2½d red	45	80	☐	
2	2	3d lilac	20	10	☐	
		p. One centre phosphor band	20	30	☐	
3		4d blue	1·50	1·10	☐	
		p. Two phosphor bands	20	15	☐	

1968–69 *One centre phosphor band (Nos. 5/6) or two phosphor bands (others). No wmk*

4	2	4d blue	20	25	☐	
5		4d sepia	20	30	☐	
6		4d vermilion ..	45	60	☐	
7		5d blue	45	60	☐	

Decimal Currency

1971 (7 JULY) *One centre phosphor band (2½p) or two phosphor bands (others). No wmk*

8	3	2½p magenta	20	15	☐	
9		3p ultramarine ..	20	15	☐	
10		5p violet	70	75	☐	
11		7½p chestnut	70	90	☐	
		Presentation Pack	2·00		☐	

For comprehensive listings of the Independent Administration issues of the Isle of Man, see Stanley Gibbons *Collect Channel Islands and Isle of Man Stamps.*

CHANNEL ISLANDS
1 General Issue

C 1 Gathering Vraic   C 2 Islanders gathering Vraic

Third Anniversary of Liberation

1948 (10 MAY) *Wmk Type* **127**   *Perf* 15×14

C1	C 1	1d red	20	20	☐	☐
C2	C 2	2½d blue	30	30	☐	☐
		First Day Cover	18·00			☐

2 Guernsey

(a) War Occupation Issues

Stamps issued under British authority during the German Occupation.

1   2   3

1941–44 *Rouletted.* (*a*) *White paper. No wmk*

1f	1	½d green	..	..	3·00	2·75	☐	☐
2		1d red ..	..	..	2·25	1·25	☐	☐
3a		2½d blue	..	..	6·00	4·50	☐	☐

(*b*) *Bluish French bank-note paper. Wmk loops*

4	1	½d green	..	..	16·00	20·00	☐	☐
5		1d red ..	..	..	9·00	24·00	☐	☐

(b) Regional Issues

1958–67 *Wmk 179   Perf 15 × 14*

6	2	2½d red ..			35	40	☐	☐
7	3	3d lilac	..	..	35	30	☐	☐
		p. *One centre phosphor band*			20	20	☐	☐
8		4d blue	..	..	25	30	☐	☐
		p. *Two phosphor bands*	..	..	20	20	☐	☐

1968–69 *One centre phosphor band (Nos.* 10/11*) or two phosphor bands (others). No wmk*

9	3	4d blue	..	..	10	25	☐	☐
10		4d sepia	..	..	15	20	☐	☐
11		4d vermilion	..	..	15	30	☐	☐
12		5d blue	..	..	15	30	☐	☐

For comprehensive listings of the Independent Postal Administration issues of Guernsey, see Stanley Gibbons *Collect Channel Islands and Isle of Man Stamps.*

3 Jersey

(a) War Occupation Issues

Stamps issued under British authority during the German Occupation.

1   2 Old Jersey Farm   3 Portelet Bay

4 Corbière Lighthouse   5 Elizabeth Castle

6 Mont Orgueil Castle   7 Gathering Vraic (seaweed)

1941–42 *White paper. No wmk   Perf 11*

1	1	½d green	..	..	3·75	2·50	☐	☐
2		1d red ..	..	..	4·00	2·75	☐	☐

1943 *No wmk   Perf 13½*

3	2	½d green	..	..	7·00	5·50	☐	☐
4	3	1d red ..	..	..	1·50	50	☐	☐
5	4	1½d brown	..	..	3·00	3·00	☐	☐
6	5	2d orange	..	..	3·00	2·25	☐	☐
7a	6	2½d blue	..	..	1·00	1·50	☐	☐
8	7	3d violet	..	..	1·00	2·75	☐	☐
		Set of 6	..	..	14·00	12·50	☐	☐

(b) Regional Issues

8   9

1958–67 *Wmk 179   Perf 15 × 14*

9	8	2½d red ..	..	..	35	50	☐	☐
10	9	3d lilac	..	..	35	30	☐	☐
		p. *One centre phospnor band*			20	20	☐	☐
11		4d blue	..	..	25	30	☐	☐
		p. *Two phosphor bands*	..	..	20	25	☐	☐

1968–69 *One centre phosphor band (4d values) or two phosphor bands (5d). No wmk*

12	9	4d sepia	..	.:	20	25	☐	☐
13		4d vermilion	..	..	20	30	☐	☐
14		5d blue	..	..	20	40	☐	☐

For comprehensive listings of the Independent Postal Administration issues of Jersey, see Stanley Gibbons *Collect Channel Islands and Isle of Man Stamps.*

REGIONAL FIRST DAY COVERS

PRICES for First Day Covers listed below are for stamps, as indicated, used on illustrated envelopes and postmarked with operational cancellations (before 1964) or with special First Day of Issue cancellations (1964 onwards). First Day postmarks of 8 June 1964 and 7 February 1966 were of the machine cancellation "envelope" type.

£sd Issues

18 Aug. 1958	Guernsey 3d (*No. 7*)	8·00 ☐
	Isle of Man 3d (*No. 2*)	20·00 ☐
	Jersey 3d (*No. 10*)	8·00 ☐
	Northern Ireland 3d (*No.* NI1)	20·00 ☐
	Scotland 3d (*No.* S1)	6·00 ☐
	Wales 3d (*No.* W1)	6·00 ☐
29 Sept. 1958	Northern Ireland 6d, 1s 3d (*Nos.* NI3, NI5)	25·00 ☐
	Scotland 6d, 1s 3d (*Nos* S3, S5)	12·00 ☐
	Wales 6d, 1s 3d (*Nos.* W3, W5)	12·00 ☐
8 June 1964	Guernsey 2½d (*No. 6*)	15·00 ☐
	Isle of Man 2½d (*No. 1*)	20·00 ☐
	Jersey 2½d (*No. 9*)	15·00 ☐
7 Feb. 1966	Guernsey 4d (*No. 8*)	7·00 ☐
	Isle of Man 4d (*No. 3*)	7·00 ☐
	Jersey 4d (*No. 11*)	7·00 ☐
	Northern Ireland 4d (*No.* NI2)	4·00 ☐
	Scotland 4d (*No.* S2)	4·00 ☐
	Wales 4d (*No.* W2)	4·00 ☐
1 March 1967	Northern Ireland 9d, 1s 6d (*Nos.* NI4, NI6)	1·50 ☐
	Scotland 9d, 1s 6d (*Nos.* S4, S6)	1·50 ☐
	Wales 9d, 1s 6d (*Nos.* W4, W6)	1·50 ☐
4 Sept. 1968	Guernsey 4d, 5d (*Nos.* 10, 12)	1·00 ☐
	Isle of Man 4d, 5d (*Nos.* 5, 7)	1·75 ☐
	Jersey 4d, 5d (*Nos.* 12, 14)	1·25 ☐
	Northern Ireland 4d, 5d (*Nos.* NI8, NI10)	50 ☐
	Scotland 4d, 5d (*Nos.* S9, S11)	50 ☐
	Wales 4d, 5d (*Nos.* W9, W11)	50 ☐

Decimal Issues

7 July 1971	Isle of Man 2½p, 3p, 5p, 7½p (*Nos.* 8/11)	3·50 ☐
	Northern Ireland 2½p, 3p, 5p, 7½p (*Nos.* NI12/13, NI18, NI23)	4·50 ☐
	Scotland 2½p, 3p, 5p, 7½p (*Nos.* S14/15, S20, S25)	4·00 ☐
	Wales 2½p, 3p, 5p, 7½p (*Nos.* W13/14, W19, W24)	4·25 ☐
23 Jan. 1974	Northern Ireland 3p, 3½p, 5½p, 8p (*Nos.* NI14/15, NI19, NI24)	1·50 ☐
	Scotland 3p, 3½p, 5½p, 8p (*Nos.* S16/17, S21, S26)	1·50 ☐
	Wales 3p, 3½p, 5½p, 8p (*Nos.* W15/16, W20, W25)	1·50 ☐

6 Nov. 1974	Northern Ireland 4½p, (*No.* NI17)	1·00 ☐
	Scotland 4½p (*No.* S19)	1·00 ☐
	Wales 4½p (*No.* W18)	1·00 ☐
14 Jan. 1976	Northern Ireland 6½p, 8½p (*Nos.* NI21, NI25)	60 ☐
	Scotland 6½p, 8½p (*Nos.* S23, S27)	60 ☐
	Wales 6½p, 8½p (*Nos.* W22, W26)	60 ☐
20 Oct. 1976	Northern Ireland 10p, 11p (*Nos.* NI27, NI30)	1·00 ☐
	Scotland 10p, 11p (*Nos.* S29, S32)	1·00 ☐
	Wales 10p, 11p (*Nos.* W28, W31)	1·00 ☐
18 Jan. 1978	Northern Ireland 7p, 9p, 10½p (*Nos.* NI22, NI26, NI29)	1·00 ☐
	Scotland 7p, 9p, 10½p (*Nos.* S24, S28, S31)	1·00 ☐
	Wales 7p, 9p, 10½p (*Nos.* W23, W27, W30)	1·00 ■
23 July 1980	Northern Ireland 12p, 13½p, 15p (*Nos.* NI31/3)	2·00 ☐
	Scotland 12p, 13½p, 15p (*Nos.* S33/5)	2·00 ☐
	Wales 12p, 13½p, 15p (*Nos.* W32/4)	2·00 ☐
8 April 1981	Northern Ireland 11½p, 14p, 18p, 22p (*Nos.* NI34, NI38, NI45, NI52)	3·25 ☐
	Scotland 11½p, 14p, 18p, 22p (*Nos.* S36, S40, S44, S47)	3·25 ☐
	Wales 11½p, 14p, 18p, 22p (*Nos.* W35, W39, W46, W54)	3·25 ☐
24 Feb. 1982	Northern Ireland 12½p, 15½p, 19½p, 26p (*Nos.* NI36, NI41, NI49, NI58)	4·25 ☐
	Scotland 12½p, 15½p, 19½p, 26p (*Nos.* S38, S41, S45, S49)	4·25 ☐
	Wales 12½p, 15½p, 19½p, 26p (*Nos.* W37, W42, W51, W61)	4·25 ☐
27 April 1983	Northern Ireland 16p, 20½p, 28p (*Nos.* NI42, NI51, NI60)	4·25 ☐
	Scotland 16p, 20½p, 28p (*Nos.* S42, S46, S50)	3·00 ☐
	Wales 16p, 20½p, 28p (*Nos.* W43, W53, W63)	3·75 ☐
23 Oct. 1984	Northern Ireland 13p, 17p, 22p, 31p (*Nos.* NI37, NI43, NI53, NI62)	4·50 ☐
	Scotland 13p, 17p, 22p, 31p (*Nos.* S39, S43, S48, S51)	5·00 ☐
	Wales 13p, 17p, 22p, 31p (*Nos.* W38, W44, W55, W65)	4·50 ☐

Jan. 1986	Northern Ireland 12p		
	(No. NI35)	1·25 □
	Scotland 12p (No. S37) ..	1·25 □
	Wales 12p (No. W36)	1·25 □
Jan. 1987	Northern Ireland 18p	
	(No. NI46)	1·75 □
	Scotland 18p (No. S59)	1·75 □
	Wales 18p (No. W47)	1·75 □
Nov. 1988	Northern Ireland 14p, 19p, 23p, 32p (Nos. NI39, NI48, NI55, NI63)	3·00 □
	Scotland 14p, 19p, 23p, 32p (Nos. S54, S61, S66, S75)	3·00 □
	Wales 14p, 19p, 23p, 32p (Nos. W40, W50, W57, W66)	3·00 □
8 Nov. 1989	Northern Ireland 15p, 20p, 24p, 34p (Nos. NI40, NI50, NI56, NI64)	2·25 □
	Scotland 15p, 20p, 24p, 34p (Nos. S56, S63, S68, S76)	2·25 □
	Wales 15p, 20p, 24p, 34p (Nos. W41, W52, W58, W67)	2·25 □
Dec. 1990	Northern Ireland 17p, 22p, 26p, 37p, (Nos. NI44, NI54, NI59, NI65)	2·00 □
	Scotland 17p, 22p, 26p, 37p, (Nos. S58, S65, S71, S77)	2·00 □
	Wales 17p, 22p, 26p, 37p (Nos. W45, W56, W62, W68)	2·00 □
Dec. 1991	Northern Ireland 18p, 24p, 28p, 39p, (Nos. NI47, NI57, NI61, NI66)	2·40 □
	Scotland 18p, 24p, 28p, 39p, (Nos. S60, S69, S73, S78)	2·40 □
	Wales 18p, 24p, 28p, 39p, (Nos. W48, W59, W64, W69)	2·40 □

POSTAGE DUE STAMPS

PERFORATION. All postage due stamps are perf 14 × 15.

D 1   D 2

1914–23 *Wmk Type* **96** *(Royal Cypher ('Simple')) sideways*

D1	D 1	½d	green	..	..	50	50	□	□
D2		1d	red ..	..	..	50	50	□	□
D3		1½d	brown	..	..	40·00	15·00	□	□
D4		2d	black	..	..	50	40	□	□
D5		3d	violet	..	..	2·00	1·00	□	□
D6		4d	green	..	..	25·00	3·00	□	□
D7		5d	brown	..	..	5·00	2·00	□	□
D8		1s	blue	..	.	25·00	2·50	□	□
	Set of 8 ..					60·00	20·00	□	□

1924–31 *Wmk Type* **107** *(Block* G v R*) sideways*

D10	D 1	½d	green	..	..	50	30	□	□
D11		1d	red ..	..	..	50	30	□	□
D12		1½d	brown	..	..	35·00	15·00	□	□
D13		2d	black	..	..	1·00	40	□	□
D14		3d	violet	..	..	1·50	40	□	□
D15		4d	green	..	..	10·00	2·00	□	□
D16		5d	brown	..	..	24·00	20·00	□	□
D17		1s	blue	..	..	6·00	75	□	□
D18	D 2	2s 6d	purple/*yellow*	..		30·00	1·75	□	□
	Set of 9 ..					95·00	40·00	□	□

1936–37 *Wmk Type* **125** *(*E 8 R*) sideways*

D19	D 1	½d	green	..	..	8·00	6·00	□	□
D20		1d	red ..	..	..	1·50	1·60	□	□
D21		2d	black	..	..	8·00	6·00	□	□
D22		3d	violet	..	..	1·50	1·60	□	□
D23		4d	green	..	.	18·00	17·00	□	□
D24a		5d	brown	..	.	12·00	17·00	□	□
D25		1s	blue	..	..	10·00	4·75	□	□
D26	D 2	2s 6d	purple/*yellow*	..		£190	8·50	□	□
	Set of 8 ..					£225	60·00	□	□

1937–38 *Wmk Type* **127** *(*G vi R*) sideways*

D27	D 1	½d	green	..	..	8·00	3·25	□	□
D28		1d	red ..	..	..	2·50	40	□	□
D29		2d	black	..	..	2·50	40	□	□
D30		3d	violet	..	..	10·00	40	□	□
D31		4d	green	..	..	60·00	7·50	□	□
D32		5d	brown	..	..	10·00	1·00	□	□
D33		1s	blue	..	..	55·00	1·00	□	□
D34	D 2	2s 6d	purple/*yellow*	..		55·00	3·00	□	□
	Set of 8 ..		..	..	..	£180	15·00	□	□

1951–52 *Colours changed and new value (1½d). Wmk Type* **127** *(*G vi R*) sideways*

D35	D 1	½d	orange	..	..	1·75	2·00	□	□
D36		1d	blue	..	..	1·10	75	□	□
D37		1½d	green	..	..	1·75	1·75	□	□
D38		4d	blue	..	..	28·00	9·00	□	□
D39		1s	brown	..	..	28·00	4·00	□	□
	Set of 5 ..	..	..	..	..	55·00	16·00	□	□

1954–55 *Wmk Type* **153** (*Mult. Tudor Crown and* E 2 R) *sideways*

D40	D 1	½d orange	..	..	4·00	2·50 □ □
D41		2d black	..	..	2·00	2·00 □ □
D42		3d violet	..	..	42·00	25·00 □ □
D43		4d blue	..	..	15·00	16·00 □ □
D44		5d brown	..	..	20·00	6·50 □ □
D45	D 2	2s 6d purple/*yellow*	..	£120	3·00 □ □
	Set of 6	..	..	..	£180	50·00 □ □

1955–57 *Wmk Type* **165** (*Mult. St Edward's Crown and* E 2 R) *sideways*

D46	D 1	½d orange	..	..	1·50	2·25 □ □
D47		1d blue	..	..	4·00	1·25 □ □
D48		1½d green	..	..	3·75	3·75 □ □
D49		2d black	..	..	35·00	3·00 □ □
D50		3d violet	..	..	4·50	1·25 □ □
D51		4d blue	..	..	18·00	3·00 □ □
D52		5d brown	..	..	27·00	2·00 □ □
D53		1s brown	..	..	65·00	1·25 □ □
D54	D 2	2s 6d purple/*yellow*	..	£160	7·50 □ □
D55		5s red/*yellow*	..	90·00	19·00 □ □
	Set of 10	..	..	£375	40·00 □ □

1959–63 *Wmk Type* **179** (*Mult. St Edward's Crown*) *sideways*

D56	D 1	½d orange	..	..	10	45 □ □
D57		1d blue	..	..	10	15 □ □
D58		1½d green	..	..	90	1·50 □ □
D59		2d black	..	..	1·25	30 □ □
D60		3d violet	..	..	40	15 □ □
D61		4d blue	..	..	40	20 □ □
D62		5d brown	..	..	45	45 □ □
D63		6d purple	..	..	60	30 □ □
D64		1s brown	..	..	1·40	25 □ □
D65	D 2	2s 6d purple/*yellow*	..	4·00	45 □ □
D66		5s red/*yellow*	..	7·50	70 □ □
D67		10s blue/*yellow*	..	9·00	3·75 □ □
D68		£1 black/*yellow*	..	45·00	7·00 □ □
	Set of 13	..	..	60·00	14·00 □ □

1968–69 *Design size* 22½ × 19 *mm* *No wmk*

D69	D 1	2d black	..	..	40	40 □ □
D70		3d violet	..	..	25	40 □ □
D71		4d blue	..	..	25	40 □ □
D72		5d orange-brown	..	4·50	5·25 □ □
D73		6d purple	..	..	80	60 □ □
D74		1s brown	..	..	80	1·00 □ □
	Set of 6	..	..	6·50	7·00 □ □

1968–69 *Design size* 21½ × 17½ *mm* *No wmk*

D75	D 1	4d blue	..	..	5·00	□ □
D76		8d red	..		1·25	□ □

D 3

D 4

1970–77 *No wmk*

D77	D 3	½p turquoise-blue		10	20 □
D78		1p reddish purple		10	15 □
D79		2p myrtle-green		10	15 □
D80		3p ultramarine	..	15	15 □
D81		4p yellow-brown	..	15	15 □
D82		5p violet	..	20	20 □
D83		7p red-brown	..	35	45 □
D84	D 4	10p red	..	30	20 □
D85		11p green	..	50	60 □
D86		20p brown	..	60	60 □
D87		50p ultramarine	..	1·50	40 □
D88		£1 black	..	2·75	60 □
D89		£5 orange-yellow and black	20·00	2·00 □
	Set of 13	..	..	25·00	5·00 □

D77/82, D84, D86/8 *Presentation Pack* .. .. .. 10·00 □

D77/88 *Presentation Pack* .. .. 6·00 □

D 5

D 6

1982 *No wmk*

D 90	D 5	1p lake	.. ..	..	10	10 □
D 91		2p bright blue	..	10	10 □
D 92		3p deep mauve	..	10	15 □
D 93		4p deep blue	..	10	20 □
D 94		5p sepia	..	10	20 □
D 95	D 6	10p light brown	..	15	25 □
D 96		20p olive-green	..	30	30 □
D 97		25p deep greenish blue	..	40	70 □
D 98		50p grey-black	..	75	50 □
D 99		£1 red	.. ..	..	1·50	50 □
D100		£2 turquoise-blue	..	3·00	50· □
D101		£5 dull orange	..	7·50	50 □
	Set of 12	.. ..	..	12·50	3·75 □
	Set of 12 Gutter Pairs	..	30·00	□
	Presentation Pack	..	14·00	□

ROYAL MAIL POSTAGE LABELS

These imperforate labels were issued as an experiment by the Post Office. Special microprocessor controlled machines were installed at post offices in Cambridge, London, Shirley (Southampton) and Windsor to provide an after-hours sales service to the public. The machines printed and dispensed the labels according to the coins inserted and the buttons operated by the customer. Values were initially available in ½p steps to 6p and in addition, the labels were sold at philatelic counters in two packs containing either 3 values (3½, 12½, 16p) or 32 values (½p to 16p).

From 28 August 1984 the machines were adjusted to provide values up to 17p. After 31 December 1984 labels including ½p values were withdrawn. The machines were taken out of service on 30 April 1985.

Machine postage-paid impression in red on phosphorised paper with grey-green background design. No watermark. Imperforate.

1984 (1 May–28 Aug)

Set of 32 (½p to 16p)	20·00	30·00	☐ ☐
Set of 3 (3½p, 12½p, 16p)	4·00	4·50	☐ ☐
Set of 3 on First Day Cover			
(1 May)		6·50	☐
Set of 2 (16½p, 17p)			
(28 August)	6·00	6·00	☐ ☐

OFFICIAL STAMPS

Various Stamps of Queen Victoria and King Edward VII Overprinted in Black.

I.R.	**I. R.**	**O. W.**
OFFICIAL	**OFFICIAL**	**OFFICIAL**
(O 1)	(O 2)	(O 3)
ARMY		
	ARMY	
		GOVT
OFFICIAL	**OFFICIAL**	**PARCELS**
(O 4)	(O 5)	(O 7)
BOARD	**R.H.**	**ADMIRALTY**
OF		
EDUCATION	**OFFICIAL**	**OFFICIAL**
(O 8)	(O 9)	(O 10)

1 Inland Revenue

Overprinted with Types O 1 or O 2 (5s, 10s, £1)

1882–1901 *Queen Victoria*

O 1	52	½d green	12·00	3·00	☐ ☐
O 5		½d blue	25·00	15·00	☐ ☐
O13	67	½d vermilion ..	1·50	50	☐ ☐
O17		½d green	4·00	3·00	☐ ☐
O 3	57	1d lilac (Die II) ..	1·50	65	☐ ☐
O 6	64	2½d lilac	£110	35·00	☐ ☐
O14	70	2½d purple on blue	50·00	4·00	☐ ☐
O 4	43	6d grey (Plate 18) ..	75·00	20·00	☐ ☐
O18	75	6d purple on red ..	£100	22·00	☐ ☐
O 7	65	1s green	£2500	£450	☐ ☐
O15	78	1s green	£200	20·00	☐ ☐
O19		1s green and red .	£600	£100	☐ ☐
O 9	59	5s red	£1300	£400	☐ ☐
O10	60	10s blue	£2250	£475	☐ ☐
O11	61	£1 brown (Wmk			
		Crowns)	£18000		☐ ☐
O12		£1 brown (Wmk			
		Orbs)	£25000		☐ ☐
O16		£1 green	£3750	£450	☐ ☐

O20	79	½d blue-green	17·00	1·50	☐ ☐
O21		1d red	10·00	70	☐ ☐
O22	82	2½d blue	£400	60·00	☐ ☐
O23	79	6d purple ..	£85000	£65000	☐ ☐
O24	89	1s green and red	£500	65·00	☐ ☐
O25	91	5s red	£4000	£1300	☐ ☐
O26	92	10s blue ..	£15000	£9500	☐ ☐
O27	93	£1 green ..	£12000	£6000	☐ ☐

2 Office of Works

Overprinted with Type O 3

1896–1902 *Queen Victoria*

O31	67	½d vermilion	90·00	40·00	☐ ☐
O32		½d green ..	£150	75·00	☐ ☐
O33	57	1d lilac (Die II)	£150	40·00	☐ ☐
O34	74	5d dull pur & bl	£750	£150	☐ ☐
O35	77	10d dull pur & red	£1300	£225	☐ ☐

1902–03 *King Edward VII*

O36	79	½d blue-green	£350	80·00	☐ ☐
O37		1d red ..	£350	80·00	☐ ☐
O38	81	2d green and red	£600	75·00	☐ ☐
O39	82	2½d blue	£700	£200	☐ ☐
O40	88	10d purple and red	£5000	£1500	☐ ☐

3 Army

Overprinted with Types O 4 (½d, 1d) or O 5 (2½d, 6d)

1896–1901 *Queen Victoria*

O41	67	½d vermilion ..	1·50	75	☐ ☐
O42		½d green ..	1·75	4·00	☐ ☐
O43	57	1d lilac (Die II) ..	1·50	75	☐ ☐
O44	70	2½d purple on blue	4·00	3·00	☐ ☐
O45	75	6d purple on red	16·00	10·00	☐ ☐

Overprinted with Type O 4

1902 *King Edward VII*

O48	79	½d blue-green ..	2·00	65	☐ ☐
O49		1d red	1·50	55	☐ ☐
O50		6d purple	60·00	32·00	☐ ☐

4 Government Parcels

Overprinted with Type O 7

1883–1900 *Queen Victoria*

O69	57	1d lilac (Die II) ..	28·00	8·00	☐ ☐
O61	62	1½d lilac	£100	25·00	☐ ☐
O65	68	1½d purple and green	14·00	2·00	☐ ☐
O70	69	2d green and red ..	45·00	7·00	☐ ☐
O71	73	4½d green and red ..	£100	75·00	☐ ☐
O62	63	6d green ..	£800	£275	☐ ☐
O66	75	6d purple on red	28·00	10·00	☐ ☐
O63	64	9d green	£650	£180	☐ ☐
O67	76	9d purple and blue	55·00	15·00	☐ ☐
O64	44	1s brown (Plate 13)	£425	70·00	☐ ☐
O64c		1s brown (Plate 14)	£750	£110	☐ ☐
O68	78	1s green ..	£120	70·00	☐ ☐
O72		1s green and red ..	£160	50·00	☐ ☐

1902 *King Edward VII*

O74	79	1d red	17·00	6·00	☐
O75	81	2d green and red ..	65·00	18·00	☐
O76	79	6d purple	£100	18·00	☐
O77	87	9d purple and blue	£225	50·00	☐
O78	89	1s green and red ..	£350	85·00	☐

5 Board of Education

Overprinted with Type O 8

1902 *Queen Victoria*

O81	74	5d dull pur & bl	£525	£100	☐
O82	78	1s green and red	£950	£375	☐

1902–04 *King Edward VII*

O83	79	½d blue-green ..	18·00	6·00	☐
O84		1d red	18·00	5·00	☐
O85	82	2½d blue	£500	50·00	☐
O86	85	5d purple and blue	£2000	£950	☐
O87	89	1s green and red	£35000	£25000	☐

6 Royal Household

Overprinted with Type O 9

1902 *King Edward VII*

O91	79	½d blue-green ..	£150	95·00	☐
O92		1d red	£130	85·00	☐

7 Admiralty

Overprinted with Type O 10

1903 *King Edward VII*

O107	79	½d blue-green ..	7·00	4·00	☐
O102		1d red	5·00	2·50	☐
O103	80	1½d purple and green	60·00	45·00	☐
O104	81	2d green and red ..	£100	50·00	☐
O105	82	2½d blue	£120	40·00	☐
O106	83	3d purple on yellow	£100	38·00	☐

> **Minimum Price.** The minimum price quoted is 10p. This represents a handling charge rather than a basis for valuing common stamps. Where the actual value of a stamp is less than 10p this may be apparent when set prices are shown, particularly for sets including a number of 10p stamps. It therefore follows that in valuing common stamps the 10p catalogue price should not be reckoned automatically since it covers a variation in real scarcity.

THE STAMP CENTRE

Our shop in The Strand (look for the green sign) comprises M&S Stamps and Steven Scott, two of the country's leading GB dealers offering a complete range of GB philately 1840–date. We can supply just about any item listed in this catalogue – and many more specialised items, should your interests be more varied. You are welcome to call at the shop Mon–Sat 9.30–5.30 (4.30 Sat) *or* order by post or telephone. We cover singles, sets, pages and collections of general Commonwealth and World and have a varied stock of specialised FDCs. Below is a sample of our special offers – see our 4 page advert in the middle of the catalogue – for a more extensive selection.

S0.1. SG 2 1d BLACK Good 3 margins £27.50	**S0.5.** SG 59 6d Average 3 margins £45.00	**SO.10.** SG 404 £1 Fine used £375.00
S0.2. SG 2 1d BLACK Good 4 margins £57.50	**S0.6.** SG 179 2/6d Good used £17.50	**S0.11.** SG 413a 2/6d Good used £8.00
S0.3. SG 14 2d BLUE Good 3 margins £6.00	**S0.7.** SG 181 5/- Good used £21.50	**S0.12.** SG 416 5/- Good used £13.00
S0.4. SG 54 1/- Good 3 margins £55.00	**S0.8.** SG 212 £1 Fine used £157.50	**S0.13.** SG 438 £1 Good used £295.00
	S0.9. SG 320 £1 Fine used £170.00	Good used = Fair cancel, no faults Fine used = Fine cancel, no faults Average used = Heavier cancel, small fault

THE STAMP CENTRE

Malcolm Sprei – M&S Stamps

Steven Scott

**77 THE STRAND,
LONDON WC2R 0DE
Tel: 071–240–3778
or
071–836–2341
Fax: 071–240 3778**

S.1 1948 Royal Silver Wedding Unmounted mint or very fine used £22.50
S.2 1961 CEPT Illustrated FDC £1.75

Malcolm Sprei – M & S Stamps

STEVEN SCOTT
GB SPECIAL OFFERS (120 more in the centre pages!!)

S.3 1953 Coronation Unmounted mint £6.75	**S.7** 1982 Postage dues set of 12 Perfect u/m below face! only £8.95
S.4 1963 Cable (phos) Perfect unmounted mint £9.95	**S.8** 1972 ½p Side band at left Fine used just £14.95
S.5 1964 Shakespeare phosphor Illustrated FDC great value at £7.50	**S.9** 25 different illustrated clean definitive First Day covers just £12.50
S.6 1951/2 Colour change postage dues Perfect unmounted mint set of 5 £34.95	**S.10** 25 different illustrated clean regional First Day covers just £12.50

"WEALTH WARNING" The centre four pages of this catalogue should contain our price list for you to purchase stamps at very advantageous prices – if your dealer has removed it, please telephone us and we will despatch you a copy immediately.

77 THE STRAND, LONDON WC2R 0DE
TELEPHONE: 071–240 3778 or 071–836 2341 FAX: 071 240 3778

Warwick & Warwick
Highest obtainable prices
for private treaty sales
– at no cost to the vendor.

75% Advance and the full balance within three weeks

A big claim. But one that we've proved time and again. What we're offering is a new deal for the seller. The highest obtainable prices for stamps within three weeks – and an immediate 75% advance – all at no cost to the vendor! Here's how we do it. We have a constantly increasing demand from our Private Treaty buyers throughout the world and we, therefore, urgently need to contact sellers of quality material of all types. It could be a good collection, a specialised study, an accumulation of remainders, a few good single items, covers. Postal History lots, a complete stock, a modern mint investment holding – in fact anything to do with philately. We can sell it.

Visits arranged for any property

A unique service, completely free of charge and without obligation. We can arrange to visit sellers within 48 hours anywhere in the country – practically irrespective of the size of value of the property to be sold. All you have to do is get in touch with us.

Free valuation GUARANTEED SALE

It will pay you to sell through Warwick & Warwick's Private Treaty Service because:

1. You obtain the services of professional valuers – each an expert in his field – whose interests are best served by selling your property at the highest obtainable price. It pays to have Warwick & Warwick on your side!

2. We can visit you within 48 hours – anywhere in the country – to arrange the sale of your property, subject to our assessment of its size and value. There's no obligation and no extra charge (although we reserve the right to decline to visit vendors of small properties). Overseas visits can also be arranged.

3. We give you a written valuation telling you exactly how much you will receive for your collection. This valuation is given FREE off any charge or obligation. We maintain a worldwide register of keen buyers covering every type of philatelic property. We have many buyers listed for every unpopular territory and hundreds of buyers for popular countries. We have many buyers capable of spending up to £50,000 and several with over £250,000 available. You can be sure we have a buyer, with money, waiting for your collection.

4. The sale will be completed quickly. As soon as you have approved our valuation, we will advance you – cheque or cash – 75% of the valuation. We GUARANTEE the balance within three weeks. In order to underwrite this guarantee we will even buy, ourselves, at the full valuation with absolutely no deductions. In fact, sales are often completed within two or three days.

5. If you refuse our valuation you owe us nothing except return postage or transport costs. No charge is made prior to sale (except where valuations of samller properties – £100 or less – are refused when a charge of £5 is made to partly cover administrative costs).

6. There is no commission or other charge payable by the vendor. You receive the full amount tendered in the valuation. The buyer will be charged with all commissions and any other costs. And, of course, there is no 'unsold' charge. We haven't failed so far – and we don't intend to start now!

Highest prices obtained

Currently the greatest demand is for older high quality British Commonwealth, particularly Australia & States, B.N.A., New Zealand and Pacifics, Western Europe, Japan, USA and, of course Great Britain. We can obtain very high prices for specialised collections, postal history material and dealers' stocks. Naturally larger properties are the best sellers as international buyers with unlimited funds will be interested. We can, and do, sell everything We have hundreds of overseas clients with special requirements and have consistently obtained the highest prices for practically every philatelic holding, even including so-called dead territories like Eastern Europe and South America. We will not refuse to handle any lot because it is unpopular. And we will continue to maintain this unique record for our clients in the future.

What the Vendors say

Thank you for your courteous and efficient service.
Mr. C., Ipswich, Suffo
Thank you for the prompt manner you have handled the valuation and sale of my stamps. Mr. W., Wimborne, Dors
I am delighted with your offer. Prof. G., Hong Kor
I trust that our happy association will continue for many years to come Mr. B., Lond
Astounded and delighted with such services and appraisals.
Mr. D., New Zealar
Thank you for your kind attention. Mr. N., Clydeban
Copies of these have been submitted to the Editor.

We have the buyers – do you have the stamps?

What can we sell for you? Almost everyone connected with stamps has something which is no longer required and can be turned into cash. Think about it for a few minutes – then let us know. You can either send your material to us by registered mail, call and see us at our offices, or write giving details. Or telephone Warwick (0926) 499031 and ask for a member of our specialist valuation staff. Remember we can be with you in 48 hours.

Free transit insurance can be arranged which will give you full cover for your stamps the whole time they are out of your possession. Contact us for details.

Warwick & Warwick Limited, Established 19
Private Treaty Department, Pageant House,
Jury Street, Warwick CV34 4EW.
Telephone: Warwick (0926) 499031.
Telefax: Warwick (0926) 491906.

Overseas vendors should quote our VAT no. 307 5218 76 on the outside of the package

100,000,000 STAMPS

That's right. One hundred million. Several **TONS** of stamps – literally. A chance we dare not miss. **So we took the lot.** Stamps from Armenia to Armadillos, Zululand to Zebras, from north, south, east and west. Big stamps, small stamps, old ones, new ones, red ones, black ones, square ones, round ones and stamps with funny squiggly bits on we'd never seen. They came to us loose, in bundles, on old leaves, in sheets and **IN TWO LORRIES**. Including **OLD IMPERFS BY THE HUNDREDS**, antique stamps in mint sheets, new issues from new democracies, old autocracies and ... well, countless, goodness knows how many bits and pieces from all over the place worth from pence to pounds. **1000'S AND 1000'S and 1000'S of different. TONS OF STAMPS** had been sitting there, in a warehouse on the Continent. For years and years. Our Agent said we HAD to buy it. YES, the trouble is ... **WE'VE BOUGHT IT BUT WE CAN'T SORT IT.** One hundred **million** stamps. Think of it. **WOULD YOU DARE TO PAY 1/2p EACH FOR THEM?**

You don't have to wash them. You don't have to dry them. You don't have to press them. The entire consignment **LOADSASTAMPS IN TWO LORRYLOADS is ALL OFF-PAPER.** All you need do is look at them and sort them. **Sort and Select.** Dive in and Discover. Open the envelope and OFF YOU GO. **NOT A LOSS LEADER, BUT A GENUINE OFFER. YOU CAN PROFIT IF YOU CAN SPARE JUST A FEW MINUTES A WEEK.**

Fair's fair – not every stamp is worth a fortune but overall at just 1/2p each overall, 100 stamps for 50p – 1/2p each, no more, whatever the catalogue value **ABSOLUTE MAXIMUM 5% OF CATALOGUE VALUE FOR THE LOT** it will take some beating. Where else do you see such value these days? AND ... in every lot **you will find AT LEAST one item worth ten pounds** or more – No this isn't a misprint – we guarantee **unconditionally** that in every lot you will find at least one stamp we normally sell for ten pounds or more.) Price to you same as for the rest, just 1/2p overall.

Or ... just pick a few out. Find a few and keep them – they're paid for. Because they are the better ones, they will cost you a little bit more, (that's fair, isn't it?) and, yes – there have been some "magic" finds. The Ad. Manager has been shown reports of stamps cataloguing two hundred pounds each!! But then you **DOUBLE THE VALUE by taking more FREE OF CHARGE. Pay for one, get another one free.** We repeat , WE BOUGHT IT BY WEIGHT – WE'LL SELL IT BY WEIGHT. **YOU CHOOSE SO YOU CAN GAIN.**

WHAT ELSE?? WELL, ... YOUR MONEY BACK IF YOU'RE NOT HAPPY. IF YOU DON'T LIKE WHAT YOU SEE, YOU'RE A HARD PERSON TO PLEASE, but we'll refund you, less a modest 75p contribution towards postage and packing. Our guarantee is valid wherever in the world you live.

Just FIVE POUNDS is all we ask from you to receive your first lot. **DELIVERY SAME DAY** – you don't want to wait. Mail today. We know IT WILL SELL FAST and once it has gone, we simply cannot get any more like it. **Must be the best offer in this catalogue! Just FIVE POUNDS incl post* Including one stamp alone worth double. Plus money back guarantee.**

WHAT CAN YOU LOSE? HOW CAN YOU LOSE?

RIGHT ... Here's my £5.00 incl postage and packing*. Please rush me without obligation a trial lot of your off-paper world mixture. I don't expect I shall get rich over-night, but I promise not to complain if I do! I may return it intact and in good order for any reason within 15 days for a refund and I shall owe you nothing.

NAME & ADDRESS:_____

_____

_____

Cheque encl/please charge my Access/Visa/card No. with £5.00* *(£5.00 Europe & BFPO. £7.50 incl £2.50 air p&p elsewhere) Card No. + Expiry

Date_____

GB DECIMAL COMMEMS – V.F.U.

VFU = Very Fine Used. **PHQ** cards are official Post Office postcards with a picture of the stamp on the front. They are issued in set5 with the same number in the set as the stamps they picture. **FDI's** are PHQ cards with the stamp pictured affixed and postmarked on the First Day of Issue – an attractive addition to any collection – **and most listed here are CHEAPER THAN THE USED SET, so you save money!**

Year & Issue	VFU	PHQ FDI	Year & Issue	VFU	PHQ FDI
1977 Heads Govt	.25	–	1985 Arthurian Leg	2.50	2.50
1977 Wildlife	1.25	–	1985 Films	3.50	3.50
1977 Christmas	.85	–	1985 Christmas	2.50	2.50
1978 Energy	.85	.80	1986 Industry	2.50	2.50
1978 Buildings (set)	.85	.80	1986 Halley's Comet	2.50	2.50
ditto mini-sheet	1.00	–	1986 Q. Birthday	2.75	1.75
1978 Coronation	.85	.80	1986 Nature	2.50	2.50
1978 Horses	.85	.80	1986 Medieval	2.50	2.50
1978 Cycling	.85	,80	1986 C/W Games	3.00	3.00
1978 Christmas	.85	.80	1986 Royal Wedding	.90	.50
1979 Dogs	.85	.80	1986 RAF	3.50	3.50
1979 Flowers	.85	.80	1986 Christmas (6)	2.50	2.50
1979 Elections	.85	.80	1987 Flowers	2.50	2.50
1979 Horseracing	.85	.80	1987 Newton	2.50	2.50
1979 Year of Child	.95	.90	1987 Archit/Europa	2.50	2.50
1979 R. Hill (set)	.75	–	1987 St. John	2.50	2.50
ditto mini-sheet	.75	–	1987 Thistle	2.50	2.50
1979 Police	.95	.90	1987 Victorian Brit	2.50	2.50
1979 Christmas	.95	.90	1987 Pottery	2.50	2.50
1980 Birds	.90	.90	1987 Christmas	2.75	2.50
1980 Railway	1.25	1.00	1988 Linnean	2.50	2.50
1980 London Exhib	.75	.75	1988 Welsh Bible	2.50	2.50
1980 Landmarks	1.25	1.25	1988 Sport	2.50	2.50
1980 Famous Women	1.00	1.00	1988 Transp/Europa	2.75	2.50
1980 Queen Mother	.25	.25	1988 Australia	2.75	1.75
1980 Music	1.10	1.00	1988 Armada	2.50	1.00
1980 Sport	1.10	1.00	1988 Verses set	2.50	2.50
1980 Christmas	1.25	1.00	ditto mini-sheet	6.50	
1981 Folklore	1.40	1.25	1988 Christmas	2.50	2.50
1981 Disabled	1.40	1.25	1989 Birds	2.50	2.50
1981 Butterflies	1.40	1.25	1989 Greetings	6.50	
1981 Nature Trust	1.75	1.50	1989 Food/Farming	2.50	2.50
1981 Royal Wedding	.85	.75	1989 Annivs	2.50	1.75
1981 Duke Edinburgh	1.40	1.25	1989 Europa	2.50	2.50
1981 Fishing	1.40	1.25	1989 Archaeol (set)	2.50	
1981 Christmas	1.65	1.50	ditto mini-sheet	5.00	
1982 Darwin	1.65	1.50	1989 Microscopes	2.50	
1982 Youth	1.75	1.50	1989 Lord Mayor	2.50	
1982 Theatre/Europa	1.85	1.50	1989 Christmas	2.50	
1982 Maritime	2.00	1.75	1990 RSPCA	2.50	
1982 Textiles	1.75	1.75	1990 20p Smiles pane	7.50	
1982 Technology	.75	.75	1990 Exhib/Europa	2.50	
1982 Cars	2.00	1.75	1990 Queen's Award	2.50	
1982 Christmas	1.90	1.75	1990 1d black m/s	2.95	
1983 Fishes	1.80	1.75	1990 Thomas Hardy	.40	
1983 Commonwealth Day	1.80	1.75	1990 Queen Mother	2.50	
1983 Engineering	2.00	1.75	1990 Christmas	2.50	
1983 Army	2.50	2.50	1990 Medals	2.50	
1983 Gardens	1.90	1.90	1990 Astronomy	2.50	
1983 Fairs	1.90	1.90	1990 Christmas	2.50	
1983 Christmas	2.00	1.90	1991 Dogs	2.75	
1984 Heraldry	2.00	2.00	1991 Greet/Good Luck	5.50	
1984 Cattle	2.50	2.50	1991 Science	2.25	
1984 Urban Renewal	2.00	2.00	1991 NVI Smiles pane	5.00	
1984 Europa	2.50	1.50	1991 Space/Europa	2.25	
1984 Summit	.75	.75	1991 Sport	2.00	
1984 Greenwich	2.00	2.00	1991 Roses	2.00	
1984 Royal Mail	2.25	1.25	1991 Dinosaurs	2.00	
1984 British Council	2.25	2.25	1991 Ordnance Survey	2.00	
1984 Christmas	2.25	2.25	1991 Christmas	2.00	
1985 Trains*	3.50	5.00	1992 Wintertime	2.00	
1985 Insects	2.75	2.75	1992 Greetings pane	5.00	
1985 Composers/Eur	2.75	2.75	1992 40th Anniv	2.00	
1985 Safety at Sea	2.50	2.50	1992 Tennyson	2.00	
1985 PO Anniv	2.50	2.50	1992 Events/Europa	2.00	

Our price for **VFU** refers to material in superb condition, with a light black small cds or official commemorative cancel. Wavy lines, slogan, parcel or the large packet cds would be about 1/2 to 1/ of these prices. Sets issued in **se-tenant** (joined) pairs/strips are priced and supplied as such.

Terms: C.W.O., subject unsold. **Full refund guarantee** provided returned in good order within 7 day of receipt. POSTAGE & PACKING is FREE on orders £10.00 and over – 50p extra in all other cases. N minimum order. (Export terms are: less VAT, plus postage.)

R. WARREN LTD.
Freepost, Lingfield,
Surrey RH7 6ZA, England

Tel: 0342 833413 Fax: 0342 833892

Stanley Gibbons STANDARD
Great Britain Album

Based on the popular DAVO Great Britain standard album and therefore including all the following special features.

- ★ High Capacity
- ★ Superb Quality Materials
- ★ Handmade to the Highest Specifications
- ★ Attractive Cover Design
- ★ Selected Stamp Illustrations
- ★ Professional Layout
- ★ Luxury Slip Case
- ★ Exceptional Value for Money

PLUS – we have added extra pages for the Machin definitives providing spaces for the popular phosphor band variations.

Because of its large page size and high capacity, it is able to house an entire Great Britain collection from 1840 to 1991 in a single volume and it therefore represents fantastic value for money when compared with other albums, some of which are already in three separate volumes.

POSITIVELY THE BEST VALUE
GREAT BRITAIN ALBUM ON THE MARKET

Item 5284STSG   **Stanley Gibbons Standard Great
Britain Album 1840–1991**   £29.95

Note: The 1992 supplement for the Stanley Gibbons Great Britain Standard Album (Item 5284ST92) will be published in January, price to be announced.

A GUIDE TO THE DECIMAL DEFINITIVES
Some hints on how to sort and collect them

The small-size decimal 'Machin' definitives have been around for over twenty years now and during that time have been subject to numerous experiments and changes in their method of production; not to mention the host of variants available from coils and booklet panes and a good number of unintentional errors and varieties thrown in for good measure.

This has resulted in one of the most interesting stamp issues ever with a great many collectors studying it in tremendous detail. It does not have to be complicated however and each collector can make his own decision as to the depth into which he wishes to go into it.

Taking just one stamp of each value and colour there are at present over 90 items to collect, while 'Collect British Stamps', which differentiates between the photogravure and lithographic printings and the phosphorised paper and phosphor banded issues, now lists getting on for 200 different stamps and if you add the various non-value indicator (NVI) stamps (SG 1445-52 and 1511-6) this takes the total to well over the 'double century! Beyond this there are all sorts of possibilities — gum differences, varying phosphor band widths and lengths, value positions, paper types and head sizes to mention only a few —

It is my intention in this article to take a few of these factors and describe briefly how one can differentiate between them.

Sorting Litho and Photogravure Printings

Let us take first the method of printing. This catalogue currently divides the decimal Machins into six different sections;

(a) Photogravure printed by Harrison and Sons with phosphor bands.

(b) Photogravure printed by Harrisons on phosphorised paper.

(c) Photogravure printed by Harrisons on ordinary paper.

(d) Lithographically (Litho) printed by John Waddington.

(e) Litho printed by Questa

(f) Litho printed by Walsall

There is therefore a basic distinction between stamps printed by photogravure and those printed by lithography. Sorting the two is not as difficult as it sounds and with a little experience it should become easy to tell which method of production was employed for a particular stamp. All you need is a reasonably good glass giving a magnification of x4 or more (x10 is even better!)

The image on a photogravure stamp is created from a pattern or 'screen', of minute dots which are not evident when looking at the stamp without a glass but show up quite clearly under magnification, especially in the Queen's face and around the margin of the stamp design where it meets the white background of the paper. Now look at the value; here also, what looks to the naked eye like a straight line is in fact made up of rows of tiny little dots.

'Screens' of dots are also used in the production of litho printed stamps but they are only required where the printer is attempting to produce shades and tints as is necessary in the Queen's head portion of the stamp. Where solid colour is used, as in the background of the majority of values, there is no need to resort to screen of dots and the background is printed as solid mass of colour. If you look at the margins the values of stamps produced in this way you ll not see any evidence of dots — just a clear ean break between the inked portion of the amp and the uninked white of the paper.

e tiny dots of the printing screen give uneven ges to the values on photogravure stamps (left). tho values have clean clear outlines (right).

Unfortunately this simple test is rather mplicated by the fact that on some of the first ho printed Machins, notably the early 5p values light violet and claret printed by Questa, the ckground of the stamp was produced, not by inting in solid colour but with a screen of dots. agnification of these stamps however shows e screened background of the Litho stamps to much coarser than the photogravure rsions. Strangely enough the early 2p and p values of Questa and the 4p of John addington, although having dark, solid ckgrounds all showed evidence of screening ts around the stamp margins but none in the lues so the 'dot' test remains valid.

As an aside it is worth mentioning that the gionals are a lot more complex in this regard it since there is no regional value which has en printed by both photogravure and litho, this rtunately does not present too much of a oblem.

In the same way it is also fortunate that among e litho printed Machins there are only three lues which have been produced by more than e printer, the 4p, 14p and 19p (to this list we uld also add the 1st and 2nd class NVIs and the

15p and 20p Penny Black Anniversary stamps of 1990). All of these stamps, however can be differentiated by measuring the perforations as the Questa versions are in each case perf 15 x 14 while those of Waddington (in the case of the 4p) and Walsall (all the others) are 14.

After a while it should become a fairly simple job to sort litho and photogravure printings 'at a glance', the generally softer more subtle tonal quality of the latter being superior to the flatter, harsher image which even the best litho printing can achieve.

Much of the interest surrounding the decimal Machins stems from the depth to which they can be studied and the vast number of collectable varieties which have been issued. The existence of many of these stamps can be attributed to nothing more than the need to provide values to cover new postage rates (i.e. inflation), however it is also true that, just as technology has resulted in huge advances in almost every field during the past 20 years so, it has also led to significant changes in both the techniques of stamp production and in the way in which mail is sorted and conveyed to its destination.

Leaving mail handling for the time being, let us consider some of the ways in which the 'quality' of the stamps themselves have changed over the years, commencing with a fairly simple aspect of this — gum.

Gum Types

There have been three types of gum used in the production of decimal 'Machins', Gum Arabic, Poly Vinyl Alcohol and Poly Vinyl Alcohol Dextrin.

(i) Gum Arabic ('GA') a clear shiny gum which shows up quite obviously when a light is shone across the back of the stamp.

(ii) Poly Vinyl Alcohol ('PVA') a matt white or slightly cream coloured gum sometimes mottled in appearance — almost invisible when a light is shone across it. At one time it seemed that PVA had become a thing of the past but in recent years it has appeared on certain Litho printings and also on the Enschedé printing of the 18p bright green issued in late 1991.

(iii) Polyvinyl Alcohol, Dextrin ('PVAD' or 'Dex') as PVA in general appearance except that a greenish blue tint has been added to the gum in order to make it more visible — the strength of this tint does tend to vary somewhat and in the case of some of the litho printings has been omitted altogether although, we are assured, the gum technically remained PVAD.

Changes to the Design and Paper

Initially, with a top value of 9p there was no difficulty in accommodating reasonably broad numerals in the lower left corner of the stamp. However a value such as 20½p could not easily be fitted into the same area. For this reason the numerals were redrawn in a narrower style. The 2p, 3p magenta, 4p greenish blue, 10p light orange, 26p red and 75p all exist with both styles as does the 1p although this is, not surprisingly, rather more difficult to identify. These changes (apart from the 1p) are not listed in *Collect British Stamps* but full details may be found in the Stanley Gibbons *Great Britain Concise Catalogue*.

Several values exist with the numerals shown in different styles, in each case the left hand value is the first type while the right hand is type II.

Another field which has been the subject of 'improvement' is paper. Basically there are two types; phosphorised and non-phosphorised. With only a couple of exceptions, stamps with phosphor bands were all printed on non-phosphorised paper — this in turn can split into two further types which are most easily differentiated using an ultra violet lamp.

The first decimal Machins were printed on what is known as Original Coated Paper ('OCP') a low fluorescence paper which appears slightly greyish under the lamp with the phosphor bands appearing dark grey. Only the original twelve values up to the 9p orange and black exist on 'OCP' because later the same year we saw the introduction of a new paper, generally known as 'FCP'.

Fluorescent Coated Paper ('FCP') first appeared in September 1971. FCP is pure white under the lamp with the phosphor bands again appearing grey. This paper was used for all stamps on which phosphor bands were printed from 1971 to 1991 when a new printing of the 18p bright green produced by the Dutch firm of Enschedé was issued on a new non-fluorescent paper which appears dark under the lamp (although the phosphor band, as will be mentioned later, *is* fluorescent). This may indicate a further change in the standard paper used for Machins, since the revised 'Castle' high values issued in March 1992 were also printed on non-fluorescent paper.

Stamps with Imperforate Edges

One field which is not covered by this catalogue but which is relatively easy to identify and is therefore popular with some collectors is that of stamps with one or two sides imperforate from booklet panes.

From the time the first British stamp booklets appeared in 1904, the stamps contained within them were printed in large reels, perforated, made up with interleaving sheets and covers, stitched and finally guillotined into the little booklets sold in Post Offices. Stitched booklets began to be phased out in the late 1970's being replaced by 'folder' types but once again multiple booklets were made up and then guillotined. Ideally, when the booklets were guillotined, the cuts coincided exactly with the centre of the rows of perforation holes. In practice however this was very difficult to achieve with the result that the perforations were frequently cut off the stamps producing the dreaded 'trimmed perfs'.

continued on page 132

QUEEN ELIZABETH II — COMMEMORATIVES 1953-1973

SG NO.			Un/m	Fine Used	Pres. Pack	F.D.C.
532/35	1953	Coronation	10.00 ☐	10.00 ☐	—	40.00 ☐
557/59	1957	Scouts Jamboree	5.00 ☐	5.00 ☐	—	15.00 ☐
560		Parliament	1.10 ☐	1.10 ☐	—	95.00 ☐
567/69	1958	Commonwealth Games	2.75 ☐	2.75 ☐	—	55.00 ☐
619/20	1960	G.L.O.	4.50 ☐	4.25 ☐	—	45.00 ☐
621/22		Europa	6.50 ☐	5.50 ☐	—	30.00 ☐
623/25	1961	POSB	2.50 ☐	2.00 ☐	—	60.00 ☐
626/28		CEPT	0.60 ☐	0.40 ☐	—	2.50 ☐
629/30		Parliamentary	3.00 ☐	2.10 ☐	—	26.00 ☐
631/33	1962	NPY	2.75 ☐	1.60 ☐	—	35.00 ☐
634/35	1963	Freedom From Hunger	2.85 ☐	2.50 ☐	—	28.00 ☐
636		Paris Conference	0.60 ☐	0.40 ☐	—	15.00 ☐
637/38		Nature Week	0.60 ☐	0.60 ☐	—	16.00 ☐
639/41		Lifeboat	4.50 ☐	4.00 ☐	—	30.00 ☐
642/44		Red Cross	6.00 ☐	5.00 ☐	—	35.00 ☐
645		COMPAC	3.25 ☐	3.25 ☐	—	25.00 ☐
646/50	1964	Shakespeare	4.25 ☐	4.25 ☐	12.00 ☐	11.00 ☐
651/54		Geographical	4.50 ☐	4.25 ☐	90.00 ☐	18.00 ☐
655/58		Botanical	5.00 ☐	4.25 ☐	90.00 ☐	18.00 ☐
659/60		Forth Road Bridge	0.60 ☐	0.50 ☐	200.00 ☐	6.00 ☐
661/62	1965	Churchill	0.60 ☐	0.40 ☐	13.00 ☐	2.00 ☐
663/64		Parliament	1.25 ☐	1.25 ☐	35.00 ☐	12.00 ☐
665/66		Salvation Army	1.10 ☐	1.10 ☐	—	24.00 ☐
667/68		Lister	1.10 ☐	1.25 ☐	—	9.00 ☐
669/70		Commonwealth Arts	1.50 ☐	1.50 ☐	—	12.00 ☐
671/76		Battle of Britain	6.50 ☐	4.25 ☐	48.00 ☐	18.00 ☐
679/80		Post Office Tower	0.75 ☐	0.85 ☐	2.50 ☐	7.00 ☐
681/82		UNO	1.25 ☐	1.10 ☐	—	9.00 ☐
683/84		ITU	1.50 ☐	1.25 ☐	—	11.00 ☐
685/86	1966	Burns	0.85 ☐	0.85 ☐	30.00 ☐	3.00 ☐
687/88		Westminster Abbey	1.00 ☐	1.00 ☐	16.00 ☐	6.50 ☐
689/92		Landscapes	1.00 ☐	1.00 ☐	—	7.00 ☐
693/95		World Cup	0.75 ☐	0.75 ☐	13.00 ☐	7.00 ☐
696/99		British Birds	1.00 ☐	0.50 ☐	7.00 ☐	7.00 ☐
700		World Cup Winners	0.20 ☐	0.20 ☐	—	2.00 ☐
701/4		Technology	1.00 ☐	1.00 ☐	7.00 ☐	3.00 ☐
705/12		Battle of Hastings	2.00 ☐	1.10 ☐	7.00 ☐	3.00 ☐
713/14		Christmas	0.45 ☐	0.45 ☐	7.00 ☐	1.50 ☐
715/16	1967	EFTA	0.40 ☐	0.40 ☐	1.50 ☐	1.50 ☐
717/22		Wild Flowers	1.40 ☐	0.65 ☐	3.00 ☐	2.50 ☐
748/50		Paintings	0.50 ☐	0.50 ☐	5.50 ☐	1.50 ☐
751		Chichester	0.25 ☐	0.25 ☐	—	1.00 ☐
752/55		Discoveries	0.60 ☐	0.50 ☐	2.00 ☐	1.00 ☐
756/58		Christmas	0.50 ☐	0.50 ☐	—	1.00 ☐
763/6	1968	Bridges	0.60 ☐	0.60 ☐	2.00 ☐	1.10 ☐
767/70		Anniversaries	0.60 ☐	0.60 ☐	2.00 ☐	3.25 ☐
771/4		Paintings	0.60 ☐	0.60 ☐	2.00 ☐	1.00 ☐
775/77		Christmas	0.50 ☐	0.50 ☐	2.00 ☐	1.00 ☐
778/83	1969	Ships	1.60 ☐	0.90 ☐	3.00 ☐	3.25 ☐
784/86		Concorde	0.50 ☐	0.50 ☐	2.50 ☐	1.25 ☐
791/95		Anniversaries	0.85 ☐	0.85 ☐	2.50 ☐	1.50 ☐
796/801		Cathedrals	1.00 ☐	0.55 ☐	3.00 ☐	2.00 ☐
802/06		Prince of Wales	1.00 ☐	0.45 ☐	2.00 ☐	1.25 ☐
807		Ghandi	0.30 ☐	0.30 ☐	—	1.00 ☐
808/11		PO Technology	0.70 ☐	0.70 ☐	2.25 ☐	1.00 ☐
812/14		Christmas	0.45 ☐	0.45 ☐	2.25 ☐	1.00 ☐
815/18	1970	Rural Architecture	0.75 ☐	0.75 ☐	3.00 ☐	1.25 ☐
819/23		Anniversaries	1.00 ☐	0.90 ☐	3.00 ☐	1.50 ☐
824/28		Literary Anniversaries	1.00 ☐	0.55 ☐	3.00 ☐	2.00 ☐
832/34		Commonwealth Games	1.00 ☐	1.00 ☐	2.50 ☐	1.25 ☐
835/37		Philympia	0.75 ☐	0.75 ☐	2.50 ☐	1.25 ☐
838/40		Christmas	0.50 ☐	0.50 ☐	2.50 ☐	1.00 ☐
881/83	1971	Ulster Paintings	1.40 ☐	1.50 ☐	5.00 ☐	2.00 ☐
884/86		Literary Anniversaries	1.40 ☐	1.50 ☐	5.00 ☐	1.60 ☐
887/89		General Anniversaries	1.40 ☐	1.40 ☐	5.00 ☐	2.00 ☐
890/93		Architecture	2.50 ☐	2.50 ☐	6.00 ☐	2.50 ☐
894/96		Christmas	1.00 ☐	1.10 ☐	4.50 ☐	1.75 ☐
897/900	1972	Polar Explorers	1.75 ☐	1.75 ☐	5.00 ☐	2.00 ☐
901/03		Anniversaries	1.25 ☐	1.40 ☐	4.50 ☐	2.00 ☐
904/08		Architecture	2.50 ☐	2.75 ☐	6.00 ☐	3.00 ☐
909/12		Broadcasting	2.00 ☐	2.00 ☐	4.50 ☐	2.25 ☐
913/15		Christmas	1.00 ☐	1.00 ☐	3.50 ☐	1.40 ☐
916/17		Silver Wedding	1.00 ☐	1.00 ☐	2.50 ☐	1.25 ☐
919/21	1973	EEC	1.50 ☐	0.70 ☐	3.60 ☐	1.60 ☐
922		Trees 9p	0.50 ☐	0.45 ☐	3.00 ☐	1.00 ☐
923/27		Explorers	2.50 ☐	1.25 ☐	4.00 ☐	2.50 ☐
928/30		Cricket	2.50 ☐	2.50 ☐	3.50 ☐	2.50 ☐

COMMEMORATIVES 1974–1982 contd

SG NO.			Un/m	Fine Used	Pres. Pack	F.D.C.
931/34		Anniversaries	1.60 ☐	1.75 ☐	3.25 ☐	2.00 ☐
935/38		Inigo Jones	2.00 ☐	1.10 ☐	3.50 ☐	2.00 ☐
939/40		Parliament	1.00 ☐	1.00 ☐	2.00 ☐	1.25 ☐
941/42		Royal Wedding	1.00 ☐	1.10 ☐	2.00 ☐	1.25 ☐
943/46		Christmas	3.00 ☐	0.80 ☐	3.25 ☐	2.00 ☐
949	1974	Trees 10p	0.50 ☐	0.50 ☐	2.25 ☐	1.00 ☐
950/53		Fire Service	1.50 ☐	1.60 ☐	2.50 ☐	3.00 ☐
954/57		U.P.U.	1.00 ☐	1.00 ☐	2.50 ☐	1.40 ☐
958/61		Warriors	1.50 ☐	1.50 ☐	3.50 ☐	2.50 ☐
962/65		Churchill	1.25 ☐	1.25 ☐	1.75 ☐	1.60 ☐
966/69		Christmas	1.00 ☐	1.00 ☐	1.75 ☐	1.40 ☐
970	1975	Charity	0.25 ☐	0.25 ☐	—	1.00 ☐
971/74		Turner	1.25 ☐	1.25 ☐	2.50 ☐	1.50 ☐
975/79		Architecture	1.50 ☐	1.25 ☐	3.00 ☐	2.00 ☐
980/83		Sailing	1.25 ☐	1.25 ☐	1.50 ☐	1.50 ☐
984/87		Public Railways	1.40 ☐	1.60 ☐	2.25 ☐	2.50 ☐
988		Parliament	0.50 ☐	0.50 ☐	1.25 ☐	1.00 ☐
989/92		Jane Austen	1.25 ☐	1.25 ☐	2.00 ☐	1.40 ☐
993/96		Christmas	1.25 ☐	1.25 ☐	2.00 ☐	1.25 ☐
997/1000	1976	Telephones	1.25 ☐	1.25 ☐	2.00 ☐	1.25 ☐
1001/04		Social Reformers	1.25 ☐	1.25 ☐	2.00 ☐	1.25 ☐
1005		American Bicentenary	0.50 ☐	0.50 ☐	1.25 ☐	1.00 ☐
1006/09		Roses	1.25 ☐	1.25 ☐	2.25 ☐	1.75 ☐
1010/13		Cultural Traditions	1.25 ☐	1.25 ☐	2.00 ☐	1.25 ☐
1014/17		British Printing	1.25 ☐	1.25 ☐	2.50 ☐	1.25 ☐
1018/21		Christmas	1.25 ☐	1.25 ☐	2.00 ☐	1.25 ☐
1022/25	1977	Racket Sports	1.25 ☐	1.25 ☐	2.00 ☐	1.50 ☐
1029/32		Chemistry	1.25 ☐	1.25 ☐	2.40 ☐	1.40 ☐
1033/37		Silver Jubilee	1.25 ☐	1.40 ☐	2.00 ☐	1.75 ☐
1038		Government	0.50 ☐	0.50 ☐	1.00 ☐	1.00 ☐
1039/43		Wildlife	1.75 ☐	0.90 ☐	2.25 ☐	2.25 ☐
1044/49		Christmas	1.10 ☐	0.85 ☐	2.00 ☐	1.40 ☐
1050/53	1978	Energy	1.25 ☐	1.25 ☐	2.00 ☐	1.25 ☐
1054/57		Buildings	1.25 ☐	1.25 ☐	2.00 ☐	1.25 ☐
MS1058		Buildings min.sheet	1.50 ☐	1.60 ☐		2.00 ☐
1059/62		Coronation	1.25 ☐	1.25 ☐	2.00 ☐	1.25 ☐
1063/66		Horses	1.25 ☐	1.25 ☐	2.00 ☐	1.50 ☐
1067/70		Cycling	1.25 ☐	1.25 ☐	2.00 ☐	1.25 ☐
1071/74		Christmas	1.25 ☐ ·	1.25 ☐	1.75 ☐	1.25 ☐
1075/78	1979	Dogs	1.25 ☐	1.25 ☐	2.00 ☐	1.50 ☐
1079/82		Wild Flowers	1.25 ☐	1.25 ☐	2.00 ☐	1.25 ☐
1083/86		European Assembly	1.25 ☐	1.25 ☐	2.00 ☐	1.25 ☐
1087/90		Horse Racing	1.25 ☐	1.40 ☐	2.00 ☐	1.50 ☐
1091/94		Year of the Child	1.90 ☐	1.40 ☐	2.25 ☐	2.00 ☐
1095/98		Rowland Hill	1.25 ☐	1.25 ☐	2.00 ☐	1.25 ☐
MS1099		Rowland Hill min.sheet	1.25 ☐	1.25 ☐	—	1.25 ☐
1100/03		Police	1.25 ☐	1.25 ☐	2.00 ☐	1.25 ☐
1104/08		Christmas	1.50 ☐	1.50 ☐	2.25 ☐	1.50 ☐
1109/12	1980	Birds	1.50 ☐	1.40 ☐	2.00 ☐	1.40 ☐
1113/17		Railways	1.50 ☐	1.10 ☐	2.50 ☐	1.60 ☐
1118		London 50p	1.50 ☐	1.50 ☐	2.00 ☐	1.50 ☐
MS1119		London 1980 min.sheet	1.50 ☐	1.50 ☐	→	1.50 ☐
1120/24		Landmarks	1.75 ☐	1.75 ☐	2.50 ☐	1.75 ☐
1125/28		Authoresses	1.50 ☐	1.50 ☐	2.50 ☐	1.50 ☐
1129		Queen Mother's 80th	0.50 ☐	0.50 ☐	—	0.60 ☐
1130/33		Conductors	1.50 ☐	1.50 ☐	2.00 ☐	1.50 ☐
1134/37		Sports	1.50 ☐	1.50 ☐	2.00 ☐	1.50 ☐
1138/42		Christmas	1.75 ☐	1.75 ☐	2.25 ☐	1.75 ☐
1143/46	1981	Folklore	2.00 ☐	2.00 ☐	2.50 ☐	2.00 ☐
1147/50		Year of the Disabled	2.00 ☐	2.00 ☐	2.50 ☐	2.00 ☐
1151/54		Butterflies	2.00 ☐	2.00 ☐	2.50 ☐	2.00 ☐
1155/59		National Trust	2.50 ☐	2.50 ☐	3.25 ☐	2.50 ☐
1160/61		Royal Wedding	1.25 ☐	1.25 ☐	2.00 ☐	2.25 ☐
1162/65		Duke of Edinburgh	2.00 ☐	2.00 ☐	2.50 ☐	2.00 ☐
1166/69		Fishing	2.00 ☐	2.00 ☐	2.50 ☐	2.00 ☐
1170/74		Christmas	2.25 ☐	2.25 ☐	2.75 ☐	2.25 ☐
1175/78	1982	Darwin	2.25 ☐	2.25 ☐	3.00 ☐	2.25 ☐
1179/82		Youth Organisations	2.75 ☐	2.75 ☐	3.50 ☐	2.75 ☐
1183/86		Europa	2.75 ☐	2.75 ☐	3.25 ☐	2.75 ☐
1187/91		Maritime	3.00 ☐	3.00 ☐	3.50 ☐	3.00 ☐
1192/95		Textiles	2.50 ☐	2.50 ☐	3.25 ☐	2.50 ☐
1196/97		Information Technology	1.25 ☐	1.25 ☐	2.00 ☐	1.50 ☐
1198/1201		Cars	3.50 ☐	3.75 ☐	4.25 ☐	3.75 ☐
1202/06		Christmas	3.00 ☐	3.00 ☐	3.50 ☐	3.00 ☐

MINT AND USED PHQ CARDS ALSO AVAILABLE

COMMEMORATIVES 1983-1990 contd

SG NO.			Un/m	Fine Used	Pres. Pack	F.D.C.
1207/10	1983	Fishes	2.50	2.50	3.25	2.75
211/14		Commonwealth Day	2.50	2.50	3.25	2.50
1215/17		Europa	2.75	2.75	3.50	2.75
1218/22		Army Uniforms	3.25	3.25	4.25	3.50
1223/26		Gardens	2.75	2.75	3.50	2.75
1227/30		Fairs	2.75	2.75	3.50	2.75
1231/35		Christmas	3.00	3.00	3.50	3.00
1236/39	1984	Heraldic Arms	3.00	3.00	3.50	3.00
1240/44		Cattle	3.25	3.25	4.25	3.50
1245/48		Urban Renewal	2.75	2.75	3.50	3.00
1249/52		Europa	3.00	3.00	4.25	3.00
1253		Summit	1.25	1.25	—	2.25
1254/57		Meridian	3.00	3.00	3.75	3.00
1258/62		First Mail Coach Run	3.00	3.00	3.75	3.00
1263/66		British Council	3.25	3.25	4.00	3.50
1267/71		Christmas	3.50	3.50	4.00	3.50
1272/76	1985	Trains	5.00	5.00	7.50	6.00
1277/81		Insects	4.00	4.00	5.00	4.25
1282/85		Europa	4.25	4.25	5.00	4.25
1286/89		Safety at Sea	3.25	3.25	4.25	4.00
1290/93		Mail Service	3.25	3.25	4.25	4.00
1294/97		Arthurian Legends	3.50	3.50	4.75	4.00
1298/1302		British Film Year	5.00	5.00	6.00	5.25
1303/07		Christmas	3.75	3.75	4.50	4.00
1308/11	1986	Industry Year	3.00	3.00	4.00	4.50
1312/15		Halley's Comet	3.50	3.50	4.50	5.00
1316/19		H.M. Birthday	4.00	4.00	5.00	4.75
1320/23		Europe	3.75	3.75	5.00	4.75
1324/27		Doomsday Book	3.75	3.75	5.00	4.25
1328/32		Sport	4.50	4.00	5.25	5.75
1333/34		Royal Wedding	1.50	1.50	2.50	2.50
1335		Conference	1.50	1.50	—	2.25
1336/40		R.A.F.	5.00	4.50	6.00	5.00
1341/46		Christmas	4.00	4.00	5.00	5.25
1347/50	1987	Flowers	3.50	3.50	4.50	4.25
1351/54		Issac Newton	3.50	3.50	4.50	4.25
1355/58		Europa	3.50	3.50	4.50	4.25
1359/62		St.John's Ambulance	3.50	3.50	4.50	4.25
1363/66		Heraldry	3.50	3.50	4.50	4.25
1367/70		Victorian Britain	3.50	3.50	4.50	4.25
1371/74		Pottery	3.50	3.50	4.50	4.25
1375/79		Christmas	3.75	3.75	4.50	4.25
1380/83	1988	Linnean Society	3.25	3.25	4.50	4.00
1384/87		Welsh Bible	3.25	3.25	4.50	4.00
1388/91		Sport	3.25	3.25	4.50	6.00
1392/95		Europa	3.25	3.25	4.50	4.25
1396/99		Australia	3.25	3.25	4.25	4.25
1400/04		Armada	2.75	2.75	4.00	3.75
1405/06		Edward Lear	3.25	3.25	4.50	4.00
MS1409		Edward Lear Min.Sheet	12.00	7.50	—	8.00
1414/18		Christmas	3.50	3.50	4.25	4.25
1419/22	1989	Birds	3.50	3.50	4.50	4.00
1423/27		Greetings	14.00	10.00	—	10.00
1428/31		Food and Farming	3.25	3.25	4.50	4.25
1432/35		Anniversaries	3.00	3.00	4.50	4.25
1436/39		Europa (Toys)	3.25	3.25	4.50	4.25
1440/43		Architecture	3.00	3.00	4.50	4.25
MS1444		Architecture min.sheet	8.00	6.00	—	6.00
1453/58		Microscopical Society	3.00	3.00	4.00	5.00
1457/61		Lord Mayor's Show	2.75	2.75	4.25	3.75
1462/66		Christmas	3.25	3.25	4.50	4.00
1467/78	1990	Penny Black	15.00	15.00	5.75	6.00
1479/82		R.S.P.C.A.	3.00	3.00	5.00	5.25
1483/92		Smiles	12.00	10.00	—	12.00
1493/96		Europa	3.00	3.00	4.00	4.25
1497/1500		Queen's Award	3.00	3.00	4.00	4.50
MS1501		London 1990 min.sheet	3.25	3.25	—	5.50
1502/05		Kew Gardens	3.25	3.50	4.00	4.50
1506		Thomas Hardy	0.60	0.70	1.75	2.00
1507/10		Queen Mother's 90th	3.25	3.50	4.50	5.50
1517/21		Gallantry Awards	3.00	3.00	4.00	4.50
1522/25		Astronomy	3.00	3.00	4.00	4.00
1526/30		Christmas	3.50	3.50	4.25	4.25

WE ALSO HOLD A GOOD STOCK OF GB DECIMAL BOOKLETS — SEND US A LIST OF YOUR REQUIREMENTS

SG NO.			Un/m	Fine Used	Pres. Pack	F.D.C.
1531/35	1991	Dogs	4.00 ☐	4.00 ☐	4.25 ☐	5.00 ☐
1536/45		Greetings	7.00 ☐	5.50 ☐	—	8.50 ☐
1546/49		Scientific Achievements	2.75 ☐	2.75 ☐	3.50 ☐	4.00 ☐
1550/59		Greetings (Type II)	3.25 ☐	3.50 ☐	—	7.50 ☐
1560/63		Europa	2.75 ☐	2.75 ☐	4.00 ☐	4.00 ☐
1564/67		Games/Rugby	2.75 ☐	2.75 ☐	3.50 ☐	4.00 ☐
1568/72		Roses	4.00 ☐	4.00 ☐	4.50 ☐	4.50 ☐
1573/77		Dinosaurs	4.00 ☐	4.00 ☐	4.50 ☐	4.50 ☐
1578/81		Ordinance Survey	2.75 ☐	2.75 ☐	4.00 ☐	4.25 ☐
1582/86		Christmas	4.00 ☐	4.00 ☐	4.25 ☐	4.50 ☐
1587/91	1992	Wintertime	2.00 ☐	2.25 ☐	2.50 ☐	4.75 ☐
1592/1601		Greetings	2.50 ☐	4.00 ☐	4.00 ☐	7.00 ☐
1602/06		Accession	1.75 ☐	2.00 ☐	2.25 ☐	4.00 ☐
1607/10		Tennyson	1.75 ☐	1.90 ☐	2.40 ☐	4.00 ☐
1615/19		Europa	2.10 ☐	2.50 ☐	2.50 ☐	4.50 ☐
1620/23		Civil War	1.75 ☐	2.00 ☐	2.40 ☐	4.00 ☐
1624/28		Gilbert & Sullivan	2.00 ☐	2.25 ☐	2.50 ☐	4.75 ☐

PHOSPHOR ISSUES

631p/33p	1962	N.P.Y.	24.00 ☐	21.00 ☐	—	95.00 ☐
634p/35p	1963	Freedom from Hunger	24.00 ☐	23.00 ☐	—	30.00 ☐
636p		Paris Conference	6.50 ☐	6.50 ☐	—	25.00 ☐
637p/38p		Nature Week	4.00 ☐	3.50 ☐	—	30.00 ☐
639p/41p		Lifeboat Conference	32.00 ☐	28.00 ☐	—	40.00 ☐
642p/44p		Red Cross	55.00 ☐	50.00 ☐	—	65.00 ☐
645p		COMPAC	18.00 ☐	20.00 ☐	—	30.00 ☐
646p/49p	1964	Shakespeare	15.00 ☐	14.00 ☐	—	12.00 ☐
651p/54p		Geographical	24.00 ☐	24.00 ☐	—	30.00 ☐
655p/58p		Botanical	24.00 ☐	24.00 ☐	—	32.00 ☐
659p/60p		Forth Road Bridge	5.50 ☐	6.00 ☐	—	12.00 ☐
661p/62p	1965	Churchill	3.25 ☐	3.75 ☐	—	4.50 ☐
663p		700th Parliament	0.40 ☐	0.40 ☐	—	16.00 ☐
665p/66p		Salvation Army	3.75 ☐	4.25 ☐	—	24.00 ☐
667p/68p		Lister	1.75 ☐	1.75 ☐	—	10.00 ☐
669p/70p		Commonwealth Arts	2.50 ☐	2.50 ☐	—	12.00 ☐
671p/78p		Battle of Britain	12.00 ☐	4.25 ☐	—	18.00 ☐
679p/80p		Post Office Tower	0.60 ☐	0.60 ☐	—	8.00 ☐
681p/82p		U.N.O/I.C.Y.	2.75 ☐	2.75 ☐	—	10.00 ☐
683p/84p		I.T.U.	6.50 ☐	6.50 ☐	—	11.00 ☐
685p/68p	1966	Robert Burns	1.25 ☐	1.25 ☐	—	3.50 ☐
687p		Westminster Abbey	0.30 ☐	0.30 ☐	—	7.50 ☐
689p/92p		Landscapes	1.00 ☐	1.00 ☐	—	7.00 ☐
693p/95p		World Cup	0.75 ☐	0.75 ☐	—	7.00 ☐
696p/99p		British Birds	1.00 ☐	0.50 ☐	—	7.00 ☐
701p/04p		Technology	1.25 ☐	1.25 ☐	—	3.00 ☐
705p/12p		Battle of Hastings	2.00 ☐	1.60 ☐	—	3.00 ☐
713p/14p		Christmas	0.45 ☐	0.45 ☐	—	1.50 ☐
715p/16p	1967	E.F.T.A.	0.45 ☐	0.45 ☐	—	1.50 ☐
717p/22p		Wild Flowers	1.25 ☐	0.65 ☐	—	3.00 ☐

WILDING SETS

515/31	1952	Tudor Crown set of 17	100.00 ☐	28.00 ☐	—	—
540/56	1955	St.Edwards Crn.set of 18	120.00 ☐	22.00 ☐	—	—
561/66	1957	1st graphite set of 6	10.00 ☐	11.00 ☐	—	60.00 ☐
570/86	1958	Multiple Crown set of 17	9.00 ☐	2.10 ☐	80.00 ☐	—
587/94	1958	2nd graphite set of 8	65.00 ☐	60.00 ☐	—	—
599/609	1959	Phosphor-graphite set of 8	80.00 ☐	70.00 ☐	225.00 ☐	—
610/18a	1960	Phosphor issue set of 17	7.00 ☐	6.00 ☐	—	—

DEFINITIVES AND HIGH VALUES

536/39	1955	Waterlow Castles	275.00 ☐	40.00 ☐	—	—
536a/39a	1958	1st De La Rue Castles	550.00 ☐	70.00 ☐	—	—
595/98	1959	2nd De La Rue Castles	150.00 ☐	17.00 ☐	—	—
595a/98a	1963	1st Bradbury Castles	13.00 ☐	8.00 ☐	—	500.00 ☐
723/44	1967-9	Pre-decimal Machins	3.00 ☐	3.25 ☐	—	6.00 ☐
759/62	1967-8	2nd Bradbury Castles	9.00 ☐	10.00 ☐	—	—
787/790	1969	Machin High Values	11.50 ☐	9.00 ☐	—	18.00 ☐
1410/13	1988	Castles	19.00 ☐	5.50 ☐	22.00 ☐	45.00 ☐
1611/14	1992	Castles	13.00 ☐	13.00 ☐	14.50 ☐	30.00 ☐

NEW MACHIN LIST NOW AVAILABLE — WRITE FOR YOUR FREE COPY

USE THESE PAGES TO INDICATE WHICH ITEMS YOU REQUIRE AND SEND TO:

Stanley Gibbons Mail Order Dept., 399 Strand, LONDON. WC2R 0LX
Tel: 071-836 8444   Fax: 071-836 7342

3b2/gen/cbslist

DIAL DIRECT
FOR HUGE DISCOUNTS!

Order direct for generous discounts from Stanley Gibbons. Use these vouchers against any purchase from SG Publications of Albums, Accessories or Childrens Starter Packs and get 10% discount off the list price.

£2.00 Discount
when spending over £20.00
Valid until Feb. 28th 1993

£5.00 Discount
when spending over £50.00
Valid until Feb. 28th 1993

£10.00 Discount
when spending over £100.00
Valid until Feb. 28th 1993

£20.00 Discount
when spending over £200.00
Valid until Feb. 28th 1993

The discount vouchers can only be used when purchasing through Mail Order. They cannot be used against a purchase of either books or catalogues.

Stanley Gibbons Publications Ltd
5 Parkside, Christchurch Road
Ringwood, Hampshire, BH24 3SH
Tel: 0425 472363 Fax: 0425 470247

FREEPHONE
0800 611622

continued from page 126
or 'straight edges' so despised by collectors. In response to complaints from collectors, Royal Mail came up with the solution, adopted long ago in countries like Canada, of not pre-perforating the stamps where they were going to be guillotined anyway.

Stamps with trimmed perfs (left) should be classed as damaged while those with true imperf margins (right) are collectable.

Thus the outer edges of the pane (or in some cases the 'long' edges of the pane only) were intentionally imperforate producing stamps deliberately issued with either one or two edges without perforations. These are quite collectable as separate stamps although they should not be confused with the earlier 'straight edges', produced by inaccurate guillotining. It is worth mentioning at this point a batch of 1st class NVI booklets produced by Walsall which contained 4-stamp panes (SG 1516) imperf at top and bottom in which the central horizontal row of perforations measure 13 instead of 14. As these were produced in error they are not included in this catalogue but complete panes and single stamps are worth looking out for.

Booklets and Coils

One last aspect of change which can be attributed purely to 'product improvement' is the number of *se tenant* booklet and coil combinations. To be sure these originated in the pre-decimal era but as postage rates have increased the number of combinations required

in order to provide a quantity of first and second class postage stamps, dispensed in a handy package for a single coin, has led to a rapid increase in the number of such panes and coils. Very collectable in their own right of course, it is these which provide some of the gems of the standard Machin collection. It is well worth while therefore keeping an eye on Royal Mail's booklet issues to ensure that you do not miss anything. Such information can of course be readily gleaned from *Gibbons Stamp Monthly* in which specialist Machin dealer John Deering keeps you up to date with all the latest news.

Technical Improvements

Let us now turn our attention to the ways in which improved (i.e. faster) mail handling techniques have affected the stamps which we collect. Basically this comes down to one word — Phosphor.

Phosphor

The twelve stamps ranging in value from ½p to 9p, issued on 15 February 1971 were all printed on ordinary coated paper and overprinted with phosphor bands, one band on the 2½p, the then 2nd class postage rate, and two bands on the other values. Since that time there have been a number of developments which have affected the phosphor on British stamps but basically they can be split into two types — phosphor printed on to the surface of the paper and phosphor which is actually incorporated into the paper coating — prior to the stamps being printed.

Taking the printed phosphor first, this is nowadays reserved for stamps covering the 2nd class postage rate plus some values which are included in booklet panes which cannot be printed on phosphorised paper. Except in error all phosphors used in the production of British stamps are 'short wave', i.e. they can only be activated by short wave ultraviolet light. This remained largely unchanged right through until the late 1980s when Harrisons developed a new phosphor ink known as 'A' phosphor or 'new' phosphor which is less obvious to the naked eye (it had been felt that the old phosphor bands detracted from the appearance of the stamps and also appears paler under the ultra violet lamp. In late 1991 a printing of the 18p, green made by Enschedé incorporated a fluorescent mponent in the phosphor band which, while it es not show up to the eye, gives a bright llow-green reaction under the lamp.

Over Phosphor

is affects only the 1p, 2p and 10p stamps and sults from an experiment in which the osphor was *printed* on to the paper before e stamp image. The three stamps concerned G X846, X850 and X887) have a matt surface d are frequently rather blotchy in appearance en held up to the light in order to show a flection off the surface. Under ultraviolet light ey show no phosphor bands and are uniformly rk in appearance.

amps on phosphor printed paper (left) have a otchy appearance when compared with osphorised paper issues (right).

'All over phosphor' is sometimes used to scribe a situation whereby, either intention- ly or by accident, a thin coating of phosphor vers the entire surface of the stamp in addition the phosphor bands. These are difficult to tect with the naked eye although, when flected against the light, the area of the stamp tween the phosphor bands is frequently ticeably darker than is normal. Such riations are of considerable interest to ecialists but fall outside the scope of this talogue. Details may be found in the *Stanley ibbons Great Britain Specialised Catalogue*.

osphorised Paper

is is often referred to as Phosphor Coated per ('PCP') or (in the case of more recent sues) Advanced Coated Paper ('ACP') but, as far as *Collect British Stamps* is concerned, all variants are covered by the term 'phosphorised paper'.

On these stamps the phosphor is incorporated into the coating of the paper and is not itself printed on the stamps at all. This method was used first on a printing of the 1s.6d. pre-decimal Machin (743c) followed by the recess printed 10p of 1970 (829). The 4½p Machin (X865) exists on phosphorised paper but this also had phosphor bands printed on top and is therefore difficult to distinguish from a normal 4½p without the phosphorised coating.

This was followed by the 8½p issued in 1976 (X938) which had a phosphorised coating without phosphor bands and from 1979/80 all new definitives from sheets and coils below the 50p value have been issued on phosphorised paper; the only values still being printed with phosphor bands being the current second class mail stamps or stamps from certain booklet panes.

Specialists differentiate between varying grades of phosphorised paper but from 1984 a more significant change over to a brighter, more fluorescent, paper was made. This is generally known as Advanced Coated Paper ('ACP') which shows up much more brightly under the ultra- violet lamp — is even brighter than FCP and with a stronger afterglow.

Warning

I hope that this article has set out some of the factors which make the decimal Machins such an interesting field to collect and study and gives some assistance in identifying the stamps concerned. If, as a beginner, the field seems complex and impossibly large, do not worry — set your own boundaries before you start. Make the decision that you will ignore any of the factors which you are not happy about and, for example, concentrate your attentions upon those variations which are plainly visible to the naked eye. It is possible however that after a few months you could be actively seeking what at present seem the most obscure varieties, phosphor screens, head types, print directions, perforator changes and any number of other features of these fascinating stamps — you have been warned!

Hugh Jefferies

VERY SPECIAL OFFERS
ALL PRICES GUARANTEED UNTIL NOV. '93 – ORDER WITH CONFIDENCE

1924 WEMBLEY (2)
U/M **£12.70**   F/U **£5.50**

1925 WEMBLEY (2)
U/M **£44**   F/U **£24**

1948 G. VI £1 BROWN
SG 478b Unmounted
of Fine Used each
£8.95

1948 WEDDINGS £1
SG 494 Very Fine Used
ONLY **£18**
Do. Unmounted **£20**

1841 2d BLUE (SG 14)
4 Margins Good Used
ONLY **£6**

1858 1d Plate Nos.
71–224 (150 stamps) Used **£159**
Do. 50 Diffferent Used **£9.95**

1988 £1–£5 (4)
U/M **£14**
Very Fine Used **£3.50**
Used **1.50**

**1984 ROYAL MAIL
POSTAGE LABELS**
Set of 32 U/M **£12**
Do. on 4 FDC's **£15**
16½p + 17p U/M **£0.99**
Do. on Souv FDC **£1.50**

OUR BEST SELLERS/COMPARE & SAVE
Please order by Ref. Number

Ref.		Price
C01	1840 1d Black, 4 Margins Good Used	£39.00
C02	do. Spacefiller Copy Used	£11.00
C03	1841 2d Blue, 4 Margins Good Used (SG 14)	£6.00
C04	1918 5/- Seahorse (SG 416) Used	£2.50
C05	1939 G. VI 2/6 Brown (SG 476) Used	£1.10
C06	do. 10/- Dark Blue (SG 478) Used	£3.50
C07	do. 10/- Brt. Ultramarine (SG 478a) Used	£0.40
C08	1951 Festival 10/- (SG 511) Used	£0.65
C09	Machin 29p (SG X1022) U/M or F/U	£1.50
C10	do. 29p (SG X1023) U/M or F/U	£1.50
C11	1988 Castle £5 Used (1 per order) (SG 1413)	£0.99

MACHIN HIVALS

C12	£1.30 (SG 1026b) U/M or F/U £3.90, Used	£1.75
C13	£1.33 (SG 1026c) U/M or F/U £4.30, Used	£1.30
C14	£1.41 (SG 1026d) U/M £4.20, F/U £2.90, Used	£1.30
C15	£1.50 (SG 1026e) U/M or F/U £2.70, Used	£0.75
C16	£1.60 (SG 1026f) U/M or F/U £2.70, Used	£0.75

C17 **G.B. 5 Reigns Mixture** (Unsorted 'as it comes')
Pre 1950's mainly on paper, some Queen Victoria/
Edward VII, George V 1912/24/34, Edward VIII, and
George VI, each lot will include 5/- Seahorse, and
George VI 2/6. 5/- and 10/-. Approx. 120 grams which
contains circa 950 stamps. Unsorted for Shades,
Perfins, Watermark Variations and Postmarks.
Super Value (3 lots for £39.00) £14.00

C18	1992 New Castles (SG 1611–14) 4 values Fine Used	£3.50
C19	Do. Good Commercially Used	£2.50
C20	Pre-1971 G.B. High Value Commems (over 6d) 500 Assorted Mint in Blocks etc.	£27.00
C21	1988 Castles to £5 in Cylinder Blocks of 4	£60.00
C22	Scotland 1960 3d 2 Bands (SG Slp) U/M	£5.00
C23	1948 Olympics on Souv. FDC with Special Postmark	£8.50

All FDC's and Pres. Packs Available. Ask for list.

FREE 80 PAGE PRICE LIST
BEST PRICES AND TOP QUALITY
"COMPARE AND SAVE"

We sell every stamp listed in this catalogue.

ASK FOR OUR LATEST LIST!

MINIMUM ORDER £10.00. SATISFACTION OR REFUND (7
DAYS). ALL ORDERS POSTPAID (Recorded Delivery Add 30p,
Registration Add £1.90)
TELEPHONE AND CREDIT CARD ORDERS WELCOME.

RUSHSTAMPS (RETAIL) LTD, PO BOX 1, LYNDHURST, HANTS. SP43 7PP
(POSTAL ONLY)   **TEL: (0703) 282044   FAX: (0703)282981**